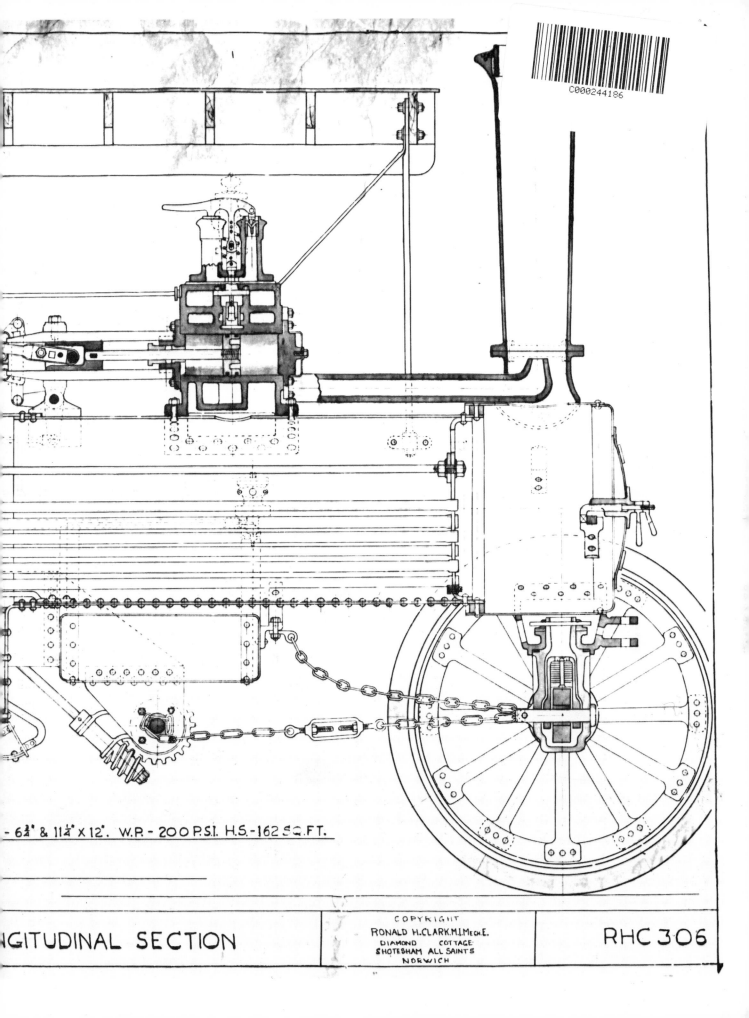

C000244186

- 6¾" & 11¼" X 12". W.P. - 200 P.S.I. H.S. -162 SQ.FT.

NGITUDINAL SECTION

COPYRIGHT
RONALD H.CLARK.M.I.MECH.E.
DIAMOND COTTAGE
SHOTESHAM ALL SAINTS
NORWICH

RHC 306

THE
Steam Engine Builders
OF NORFOLK

RONALD H CLARK MI MechE

Zoe's First Birthday
Present for
Grandad
Lots of Love

ZOe   (Helped by Daddy)
XXX

Foulis

Haynes
®

ISBN 0 85429 678 6
©Ronald H. Clark.
First published October 1988

All rights reserved. No part of this book may be reproduced or transmitted in any form or by any means, electronic or mechanical, including photocopying, recording, or by any information storage or retrieval system, without permission of the Publisher.

A FOULIS book

Published by:
Haynes Publishing Group
Sparkford, Nr. Yeovil Somerset, BA22 7JJ, England

Haynes Publications Inc,
861, Lawrence Drive, Newbury Park, California, 91320, USA

British Library Cataloguing in Publication Data
Clark, Ronald H. (Ronald Harry), *1903–*
 Steam engine builders of Norfolk.
 1. Norfolk. Steam locomotive industries
 I. Title
 338.7'62526'094261
 ISBN 0-85429-678-6

Editor: Jeff Clew
Cover Design: Camway Autographics
Main colour transparency: Peter Nicholson
Page layout: Chris Hull
Printed in England by J. H. Haynes & Co. Ltd.

Publisher's Note
Some of the original photographs and line drawings reproduced in this book are very old and often damaged or of poor quality such that even with the most sophisticated of modern equipment their quality leaves much to be desired. Because authenticity is of paramount importance in a work of this nature it has taken precedence over clarity of reproduction and justified their inclusion.

To my late Wife

GLADYS DAVIES CLARK
(née Leckenby)

1896 – 1981

"I am sure you will agree with me in thinking that the simplification on machinery always adds to its beauty".

George Stephenson
12th November 1821

In fitness for the urgent hour
Unlimited untiring power,
Precision, promptitude command
The infant wills the giant hand.
Steam, mighty Steam, ascends the throne
And reigns Lord Paramount alone!

William Harrison

ACKNOWLEDGEMENTS

David C. Bretten Esq. Fig 9
Alan Bloom Esq. Fig 349
Lt. Col. R. F. H. Burrell. Fig 108
H. O. Clark, The late. Fig 207
C. A. Cushion Esq. The late. Fig 325
David Jones. Bridewell Museum, Norwich. Fig 331
David H. King Esq. Figs 214–222
Dr. J. L. Middlemiss. Figs 303, 305 & details for Fig 306
M. & G. N. Circle. Fig 234
T. B. Paisley Esq. The late. Fig 31
G. S. Soame, The late. Fig 320
Robert Tidman, The late. Fig 334
R. Trett. The Museum, Lynn. Figs 190, 193, 194, 311
George Watkins Esq. Fig 1

In addition, notes and information from several owners and partners both living and deceased, in various forms.

CONTENTS

List of Firms

PREFACE

The kind reception afforded my previous three county Steam Engine Builders, Norfolk 1948, Suffolk, Essex & Cambridgeshire 1950 and Lincolnshire 1955 – they have been out of print for many years now – had encouraged me to re-write completely the Norfolk book. Since 1948 much information hitherto unkown, new photographs and old drawings have come to light, enabling me to expand the illustrations to no less than 349 and the latest total of firms involved is now 42.

As before, the reader will find the firms listed in numerical and alphabetical order. Roman numerals are used in this case to be distinct from all dimensions in the text which are exclusively in ordinary numerals or figures.

The earliest engine mentioned would be the portable by Charles Burrell in 1846. Many of the usual types were made by the Norfolk Builders, between them covering vertical, horizontal, marine, crank-overhead, beam, portable, traction and roundabout centre engines, road and rail locomotives and steam wagons. Two uncommon types on the other hand must not be forgotten – the vee twin and the grasshopper. The vee four uniflow car engine illustrated is, of course, a natural development from the vee twin. Happily, there are two firms presently prepared to build steam engines for commercial applications, as distinct from models, to order.

In many cases the illustrations are off firm's own original catalogue blocks salvaged by the author over a period of years and in others, from photographs of actual engines now, many of then, gone to the scrap heap.

It is, of course, impracticable to preserve every example of the steam engine builder's skill but it is a pity that more of the interesting types have not been preserved *in situ* so that the right atmosphere is retained. This can be done as exemplified by the pumping engines at Stretham in 1831, Pinchbeck 1833 and Dogdyke 1856. The Dogdyke engine is no mere lifeless exhibit so common to museums run officially, but can be enjoyed in steam on many Sundays during the period of summer time.

The steam engine in all sizes and types was the common prime-mover for most of the last century, its successor being the internal combustion engine in various forms. It is interesting to speculate therefore why forty two firms were at one time engaged in the county on steam engine production, whilst none in this county are now interested in making examples of its successor - the oil engine. I am not so sanguine as to suppose that even now everyone who made a com-mercial steam engine is included. There may still be "one-off" engines I have never heard of and if so, perhaps data may be forthcoming.

In searching for details of engineering history for this book – and others – it has been brought home to me very forcibly how very quickly historical information becomes lost or forgotten and relevant literature destroyed. I must emphasise that some of the information in the following pages was obtained only just in time. In fact I have met at times a curious sense of shame that those concerned were at one time connected with steam engines at all! And this in the land of its origin! To illustrate this, on one summer meeting The Newcomen Society were not granted permission to view a fine uniflow engine of over 1,200 hp. I learned later that the well-known firm concerned were afraid that if too many people knew they were still driving the mill by a steam engine – such machines now being considered out of date – it would be bad for their image! British Rail at one time must have had the same outlook.

Why must England be so ashamed that she once led the World in steam engine building? It therefore behoves all those interested to record what data they can and to preserve all official literature – sometimes not valued even by the firm concered – when they obtain it.

Norfolk possesses a charm denied those whose cursory knowledge of it may be gleaned only from the A47, A11 and one or two similar congested roads. It is a charm which demands return visits from personalities who once come under its spell, and I am pleased to say the researches necessary to enable me to re-write this book have been the occasion for many return visits. They have taken me to many parts of this large and varied county, accounting for many happy miles by motorcycle, thereby enhancing the task and making the work a pleasure.

RONALD H. CLARK.

Diamond Cottage
SHOTESHAM ALL SAINTS
Norwich.

JOHN C. ARCHER, 11 Calvert Street, NORWICH.

John Crickmore Archer used at one time a relatively small shop at 11 Calvert Street in Norwich where he built, probably to order, a small number of horizontal and vertical engines and reputedly, one or two portables. His range was from 1 to 12 nhp and one vertical worked for many years at Messrs. Adcock & Denhams in Queen Street, Norwich. Unfortunately little detailed information has been discovered about these three types.

However, he also built a small beam engine of which a photograph is reproduced in Fig 1, the cylinder of which was 5⅛in x 8in, the beam centres being 31⅝in. For many years this engine drove the smith's shop at Bagshaw's Bone Works, now demolished, at Haddiscoe, Norfolk. After it had fallen into disuse it was donated to the Norwich Society of Model Engineers and preserved in their headquarters in the Old Gothic Works, King

Fig 1 Small beam engine by John C. Archer.

Fig 2 Drawing of Archer's beam engine.

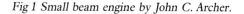

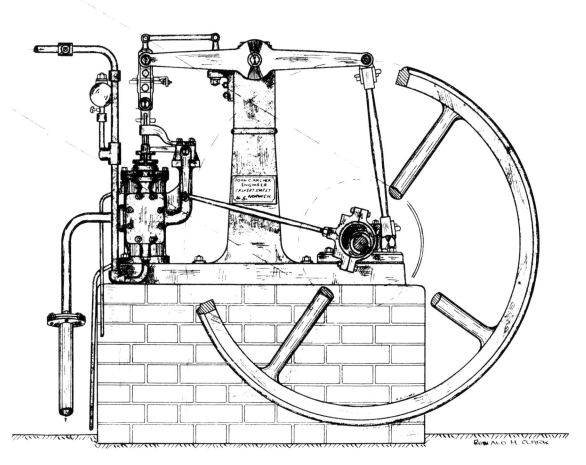

Street until so unfortunately it was destroyed by enemy action in 1942. The Old Gothic Works will be mentioned again later when dealing with Laurence, Scott & Co. Ltd.

One point worthy of mention is the Watt parallel motion used where the coupler is divided externally and the piston rod attached at the external generating point more clearly seen in the drawing in Fig 2, fortunately prepared by the author before destruction. The maker's brass nameplate should be noted on the side of the solid cast iron standard. This was one of the few beam engines built in the county.

II

W. P. BAKER, Phoenix Works, KING'S LYNN

This, probably the smallest Lynn firm to make steam engines, was established by Robert Southgate Baker as early as 1839 at Union Place, Austin Street, off Blackfriar's Road. At this early period he was described as an iron and brass founder, machine and engine builder. In 1854 he had moved to larger premises in Blackfriar's Road. By 1877 his son William Philip Baker was in charge of the business. The founder had called his small works Phoenix Foundry and where possible his castings bore a Phoenix Displayed in relief. Later on we shall see that Alfred Dodman (No XIV) took over Baker's original premises when the former started on his own account.

As early as 1865 Baker senior had produced a few portables but no details of them appear to have survived. However c1880 he completed a nicely proportioned crank-overhead engine for Ramsden's Estate in Middleton Fen, just east of Lynn, to drive a scoop wheel draining that level. It is shown in Fig 3 with the piston nearly at the top of its stroke. The cylinder was 6½in x 9½in and worked non-condensing with a flywheel 5ft 0in diameter having a crowned face. On the valve chest cover was the Phoenix Displayed. Its main dimensions are given in the diagram in Fig 4. A vertical boiler was in an annexe near the scoop wheel and the heavily lagged steam pipe is in the foreground in the photograph.

The scoop wheel was 16 feet diameter with 40 paddles or floats 3ft 3in long x 5¼in wide, having the iron centre of the wheel in eight segments bolted together. The drive was by spur gearing as shown in the diagram, the crankshaft pinion having six teeth and the gear on the scoop wheel 90 teeth, giving a ratio of 15 : 1 down from the engine. All teeth had a circular pitch of 1⅝in x 2¾in long.

Sadly, this neat little unit ceased work in 1934 and has since been destroyed.

Fig 3 Crank-overhead engine by Baker of Lynn.

Fig 4 Diagram of dimensions of Baker's engine.

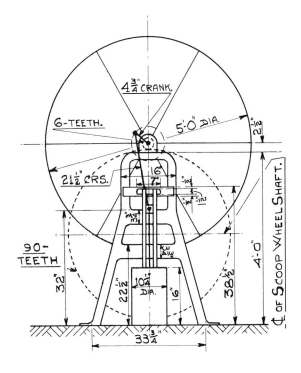

III

ROBERT BARNES,
Southtown Road, GREAT YARMOUTH

Robert Barnes had established his small works by 1865 in Southtown Road, close to Southtown railway station. By 1879 he had moved to Southtown Ironworks in the same road and some years later his old premises became occupied by Messrs. Crabtree (see No XI). He was classified as an Engineer, Millwright, Boiler Maker and Machinist.

Apparently he specialised in crank-overhead and horizontal engines and a good example of the former type is to be seen in Fig 5 which for many years worked in Messrs. Stanton's Timber Works in Lynn. The single cylinder was 7in x 18in making a timed speed of 43 rpm with steam at 35 psi. The valve chest contained a short D slide valve worked by one eccentric and was therefore non-reversing; curiously the connecting rod drove on to a crankpin fixed in a small boss on one spoke of the flywheel, which was six feet diameter. Owing to an

Fig 5 A crank-overhead engine by Robert Barnes.

Fig 6 Pump crank fixing on the engine in Fig 5.

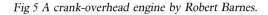

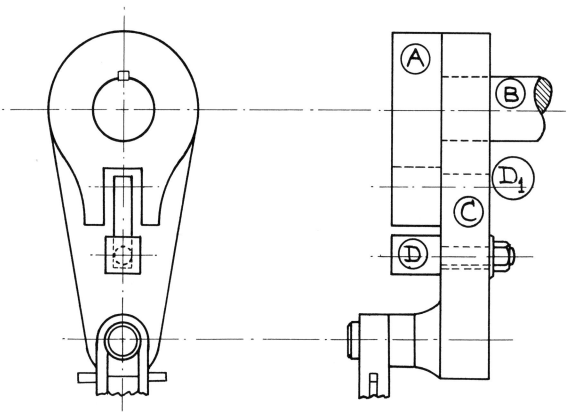

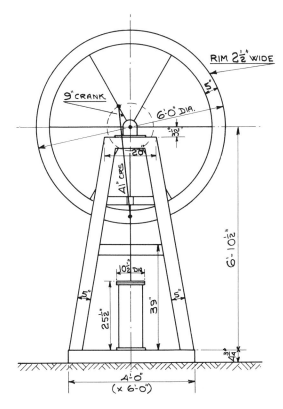

Fig 7 Diagram of dimensions of Barnes's crank-overhead engine.

Fig 8 A fine horizontal pumping engine by Robert Barnes.

amount of whip which takes place with this form of spoke crankpin, the speed mentioned was found to be the smoothest for normal running. On the middle of the crankshaft and between the A frames are four throws for four small pumps for pumping creosote under pressure into the timber containers. At the far end of the crankshaft and outside the A frame was another but larger pump used for expelling air, when necessary. The method of attaching this pump drive is very clever and is illustrated in the diagram in Fig 6. The half-crank A is keyed to the crankshaft and always rotates with it. The false crank C is a free turning fit on the crankshaft B and has in it a slot in which there is a square-headed bolt secured with a nut and a washer behind the crank. The normal disconnected position is as in D but if connection is required the nut is slackened and the bolt returned into position D1 when the two cranks rotate as one. The height from ground level to the centre-line of the crankshaft was 6ft 10½in as seen in the diagram in Fig 7 which also gives other important dimensions.

A horizontal engine is shown in Fig 8 and this was erected in Reedham Marsh Pumping Station, Norfolk, in 1880, having a 12in x 24in single cylinder. The valve chest-housed the usual slide valve and a Meyer expansion valve for varying the cut-off. All of the engine was carefully finished, the cylinder lagging was clad with polished sheet brass, and both crosshead guides were supported on a pair of fine turned columns seen in the photograph. Its flywheel was eight feet diameter with the rim 6¾in wide. This engine drove a vertical spindle turbine pump through two pairs of bevel gears and a countershaft. Unfortunately the whole unit has now been destroyed.

⤳ IV ⤶

BELMEC ENGINEERING LTD.,
Bridge Works, WIGGENHALL
ST. GERMANS.

A new company formed in 1968, mainly by David C. Bretten, to undertake general engineering work, particularly one-off machines and similar work.

It was decided in 1975 to produce two Savage chain traction engines, one of which is depicted in Fig 9 and from which it will be seen that the type chosen was the example where the cylinder is mounted over the firebox. The prototype is shown in Fig 257 and the particulars there given will apply to Fig 9. Modern methods of production and modern materials were used by Belmec so that the boiler and firebox are built using BSS 2790 steel, welded, and thus permitting riveted heads to stand proud in areas where they would be seen

Fig 9 A chain drive Savage-type traction engine by Belmec.

when ordinary riveting was used. Inspection was carried out during construction meriting a Certificate for Class 2.

The hornplates were flame cut from 1¾in mild steel plate to represent castings and all wheels were fabricated from steel plate and having all welds sand-blasted to remove ripples and present to the eye what would be taken for a casting. Oak and ash were used to making the fore-carriage. The cylinder and boiler lagging was of strip mahogany, covered with sheet steel cladding and finally finished in traditional emerald green. The smokebox, chimney and firebox were, of course, black, but the wheels have crimson spokes.

Another successful copy made has been of a No 6 Savage centre engine similar to that shown in Figs 300 and 301 and fitted to a set of Galloping Horses. Here again, modern methods and materials were used. The purist may be critical of such methods but one must remember that if such engines were in regular production by their original makers today, then one can imagine old established concerns using most advantageously the latest techniques available. As the reader progresses he will meet many instances of nearly a century ago where the maker stressed that the most up-to-date machinery and materials are employed.

David Bretten tells me he personally re-drew all the necessary drawings to update them to modern methods of manufacture.

Belmec Engineering are one of only two firms in Norfolk at present able to produce certain steam engines as required and alongside other productions, in stainless and mild steel, created by thirty five or more skilled craftsmen.

✥ V ✥

THOMAS BRADLEY,
Bridge Foot Works, GREAT YARMOUTH.

This builder's small works was sited at the foot of the earlier river bridge where he commenced with the traditional small foundry and machine shop, but the exact establishement date is not known. After he retired, the premises became part of a veterinary surgery but nothing now remains.

Some of the first condensing small marine engines were constructed by Thomas Bradley and one of the first was fitted in an old river passenger boat called *Pride of the Yare.* Another powered a similar vessel *Queen of the Broads.* Accurate dimensions have not turned up but one interesting feature was the arrangement of the air and circulating pumps. One was placed at each side at one end of the engine, the plunger rods being attached one to each end of a short rocking beam fixed at its centre to the middle of the valve chest cover. An eccentric on the crankshaft connected to one end of the short beam transmitted the necessary motion. The compound cylinders would undoubtedly have been about 8in and 15½in x 8in.

 VI

CHARLES BURRELL & SONS LTD.,
St. Nicholas Works, THETFORD.

A master smith, Joseph Burrell by name, commenced his business with a forge in a small smithy in St. Nicholas Street in the year 1770. In this period Thetford, formerly the ancient Capital of East Anglia, was essentially a great agricultural centre, although it may be somewhat less so today. Burrell's forge abutted the churchyard wall of St. Nicholas church, one of the twenty churches in this ancient town. The parish of St. Nicholas had been united with St. Peters in 1547 and upon the consolidation St. Nicholas church was all but demolished, only the square tower left standing in 1738 and some parts of it in 1770. The churchyard became glebe land to the rectors of St. Peters. For many years previously to 1770 there had been a smithy in this part of the town and early in the 18th century there had been a blacksmith's shop on the hill close by the Fleece Tavern. Unfortunately the smith's name is unknown but it is known that John Draper in Thetford cast two bells for Stanfield church as early as 1629.

In 1778 Mr. Coke of Holkham originated the first of his "Sheep Shearing and Agricultural Meetings" there and such occasions continued uninterruptedly until 1821. There is no doubt these annual sheep shows at Holkham laid the foundation of the larger annual shows of the Royal Agricultural Society, the first of which was held in 1839. At these shows there were exhibited all breeds of cattle, sheep, pigs, goats and horses etc. There were too, awards for the best and most useful newly-invented or improved implement of husbandry and for the best work in ploughing. By this time the Burrell Forge was not content with just repairing agricultural machinery and shoeing but became interested in the design and manufacture of useful and new implements.

By 1803 Joseph Burrell had entered in the Holkham Show a "*new and original machine in which from the same barrel seed oil and cake manure was delivered in one tube through which it was deposited into the earth by the same coulters*". This so impressed the judges

that it won a beautiful silver cup which was awarded the following year and is illustrated in Fig 10. This is preserved by the family as an heirloom and the inscription can be read in the illustration.

Fig 10 The silver cup awarded to James and Joseph Burrell.

Earlier, Joseph Burrell had fathered two sons, James and Joseph. Both brothers were partners in a double marriage on December 10th 1803, at Norwich Market Place, where Joseph married Mary Pooley, keeper of the ladies boarding school in Thetford, and James married Miss Elizabeth Pryke, late of Barnham nigh unto Thetford.

Joseph and Mary's offspring had no connections with the firm but James and Elizabeth had two sons – James and Charles, the first of this name, who, born in 1817, took over the running of the main works in 1836 at the tender age of nineteen, and lived until 1906. At this period in engineering development, 1802, the year Joseph Burrell perfected his seeding machine, Mathew Murray of the Round Foundry, Leeds, had patented the common slide valve and Richard Trevithick had made his experimental road engine, a type of prime mover with which Thetford was to become so associated in later years. Besides the seeding machine, St. Nicholas Works produced ploughs, harrows, rakes, hurdle-making machines, sawbenches large and small and even a gorse bruising machine. This necessitated enlargement of the small machine shop and the laying down of a small foundry for iron and non-ferrous castings. This expansion spread to cover part of the glebe land of St. Nicholas churchyard. I am reliably informed that until after the World War I on a frosty morning the outline of the western tower could be traced in the yard, the square shape appearing as a different texture of the ground. Charles I, as we may call him, had five children – Frederick John, Robert George, Charles II, William and Ella. William became a solicitor and like their sister Ella, took no part in the business, which was later run, developed and managed by the three eldest sons.

Frederick John married and had one son. Robert George died prematurely in 1904, leaving a son Robert Eden tragically killed on what is now the A11 in April 1921. Charles II, born in 1847 and died in 1929, left two sons, Herbert John and Charles William Wilberforce, and a daughter Marion. Both the sons entered the firm so this second son we may call Charles III. Herbert John's son Ronald, born in 1910, entered the army and after twenty two years service retired with the rank of Lt. Colonel. Charles III also attained the same rank, but had no family. Ronald's son Peter was born in 1939 and he and his father are now the remaining male members of the famous family.

After World War I there arrived a foreseen period of trade depression although the Thetford firm felt the first impact as early as the end of 1919 when many cancellations were made from a good order book. There was, however, a curious small boom in road locomotives and wagons but this eased off considerably after 1922. This was one reason for the decline but another and far-reaching reason was that the firm joined the Agricultural & General Engineers Ltd. The AGE proved to be big business in its worst form. Incorporated as a public company on 4th June 1919, the great idea was that the Company would provide capital to extend the works and plant of such companies who joined it. Their HQ was at Aldwych House, London, and it was to deal with the buying and selling for the constituent companies. There were ultimately thirteen other firms in the combine besides Charles Burrell & Sons, who soon found out the inefficiency through buying and selling in a remote HQ. So from July 1920 the associated companies again did their own buying and from October 1922 did their own selling – as they had done for years and years prior to 1919!

Of course the inevitable happened and production had to be concentrated in fewer works. To achieve this in some measure the Thetford business was transferred to Richard Garrett & Sons Ltd., at Leiston, Suffolk in 1929. This arrangement brought forth no improvement and on 16th February 1932 Sir Gilbert Garnsey KBE, was appointed receiver and manager by the bankers. Offers were made for the shares of Messrs. E. H. Bentall Ltd., L. R. Knapp Ltd., and the assets of Richard Garrett & Sons and J. & F. Howard were

realised by the receiver appointed by these companies. No offers were made for Burrell's shares so the firm was put into voluntary liquidation. Later the Summary of the Statement of Affairs No. 99109 of 1932 was submitted to the Companies Court of the Chancery Division before Mr. Justice Bennett on 27th October 1932 and this date may be considered as the close of Charles Burrell & Sons Ltd., after 159 years of trading and engineering activity in the ancient capital of East Anglia. To give some idea of the chaotic state of the AGE's finances, at the time of closure their liabilities were £827,895 4s 1d, against the gross assets of £139,029 9s 8d!

The auction of the work's effects and plant took place on December 17th and 18th 1930 and comprised 745 lots, Messrs. Harry Hawks & Witton of Thetford being the auctioneers.

Reverting to the year 1839, this saw two important events, (1) the first of the RAS annual shows at Oxford and (2), William Howden of Boston built the first really practical portable engine. In those days the directories classified James and Charles I as "agricultural machinists". They were, of course, a lot more, being master smiths, designers, schemers, and leaders. William Howden's portable must have impressed the young Charles I because in 1846 St. Nicholas Works turned out their first portable, which is believed to be the firm's famous No 1, shown in Fig 11. The locomotive-type boiler had a haystack top over the firebox, worked at 45 psi supplying steam to the single cylinder about 8in x 12in. It was reported working as late as 1884, after which it was bought back by the firm

Fig 11 First design of portable engine by Charles Burrell in 1846.

and was exhibited in the south yard for many years. Many of this type were made and sold. 1884 was the year in which the firm became a limited liability company – Charles Burrell & Sons Limited.

Although these early portables enhanced the firm's reputation as engine builders, what eventually established their national reputation was the series of heavy road haulage engines using James Boydell's Patent Wheels. Boydell filed his first patent in 1845 but a much improved specification was filed in 1854 on the basis of which James Boydell formed the Boydell Endless Railway Company. They approached Charles Burrell with a view to him making engines for them and the young opportunist eagerly agreed to do so. The first Burrell-Boydell engine was completed in 1856 and took the form illustrated in Fig 12. Boydell's wheels consisted of a series of feet or pads hinged to the middle of the rim by a cycloidal slotted link. Being of cycloidal form the links permitted the pads to be put down, and after the wheel had passed over it, lifted it perpendicularly off the ground, the engine therefore laying down its own track. It could travel over very poor roads or in some cases, where no road existed. This engine was the first heavy duty steam road haulage engine and the main dimensions of this historic machine are as follow:-

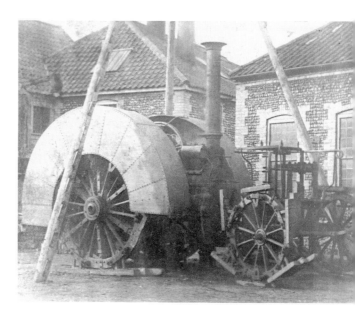

Fig 12 The Burrell-Boydell engine of 1856.

Note that the outfit is steered by means of a fore-carriage also equipped with a pair of Boydell wheels, the steering mechanism consisting of a handwheel operating a semi-circular rack and pinion.

Another view of this 1856 engine is recorded in

Date	1856		
nhp	12	Driving wheels, width over tyre	6½in
Number of cylinders	2	Gear ratios – fast	8 : 1
Bore of cylinders	7½in	Gear ratios – slow	17 : 1
Stroke of cylinders	12in	Advance of engine per foot of piston travel – fast	1·070 ft
Flywheel, diameter	4ft	Advance of engine per foot of piston travel – slow	0·50 ft
Grate area	5½ sq ft	Capacity of water tanks	315 gallon
Number of tubes	71	Capacity of coal bunker	10 cwt
Diameter of tubes	1¾in	Weight of engine, empty	9 ton 10 cwt
Water heating surface per nhp	22·8 sq ft	Weight of engine in working order	11 ton 10 cwt
Water heating surface per sq ft of grate area	49 sq ft	Weight on driving wheels	8 ton
Working pressure	100 psi	Weight on leading wheels	3 ton 10 cwt
Driving wheels	Type WI forged all in one piece. Tyres shrunk on. Boydell's patent endless railway on rims.	Overall length	17 ft
		Remarks	For heavy haulage
Driving wheels, diameter	5ft 6in		
Driving wheels, width over shoes	1ft 4in		

Fig 13 showing it in action, the trailer, also on the patent wheels, containing a load of Burrell ploughs for delivery to customers.

Fig 13 Another type of Burrell-Boydell engine.

On Thursday May 14th 1857 one of these engines left Thetford at 10.03 am with a load of 17 tons 1 hundredweight behind the drawbar and got to its destination, Stratford, Essex, early evening on Saturday May 16th. This was certainly an epic journey, being the first long distance example of heavy goods hauling ever made in this country on a main road by steam power. I trust my reader will remember this when next he traverses the A11.

Engines with such a high drawbar pull as these Burrell-Boydells were tried for ploughing by direct traction and were found to be quite satisfactory. An exhibition test was carried out on May 17th and 18th 1857 in the neighbouring village of Croxton, two miles north of Thetford, in a large field alongside the Thetford-Watton highway. In Fig 14 is an engraving showing the demonstration engine drawing four two-furrow ploughs at once. On one occasion six ploughs forming twelve furrows were successfully drawn by the engine, using Burrell ploughs, of course. In addition, subsoil and draining ploughs made under Cotgreaves Patent were also demonstrated. When visitors off the 8 am train from London alighted at Thetford they were treated to a demonstration of "Drawing Heavy Weights on Common Roads" by one of the Burrell-Boydell engines on the approach roads to the station. Another engine was shown drawing a threshing machine. Here it is opportune to mention that Charles Burrell I made and exhibited at the RAS Show in York in 1848 the first combined threshing and finishing machine ever offered to the public.

For the next year, 1857, a number of important modifications and improvements were made to the type of engine depicted in Fig 12 and these alterations may be examined in the sets of drawings reproduced. The

Fig 14 A Burrell-Boydell engine direct ploughing.

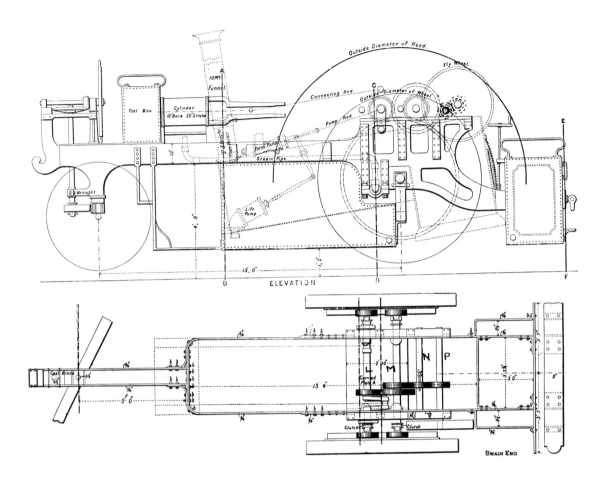

Fig 15 Details of an historic Burrell-Boydell engine.

upper view on Fig 15 shows a general outline and the lower details of the engine in plan, and in particular the gearing where the crankshaft L carries a pinion each end and one in the centre. The centre pinion meshes with a gear on the countershaft M which too, carries a pinion each end. All four pinions on both crank and counter shafts engage with the large toothed ring on the driving wheels, from which they can be disengaged by means of the dog clutches operated by hand levers. Close to the gear on the countershaft is another driving pinion meshing with a smaller gear on the fourth or flywheel shaft P. These inner gears are fixed in mesh, otherwise the flywheel would not be connected to the crankshaft. There are therefore two road speeds, top when the crankshaft driving pinions engage direct in the driving wheels rings, and low gear when the crankshaft pinions are clutched out of gear, enabling the drive to be taken on to the clutch and its pinions.

Both duplex cylinders were 10in x 20in and it was this long stroke which produced the considerable

turning moment converted to drawbar pull. The general outline shows another ingenious feature, viz. the means whereby the boiler could be inclined as required on steep hills to keep the water level horizontal and therefore the firebox crown properly covered. A curved toothed rack was fitted to the after end of the firebox with which meshes a worm mounted on a nearly vertical shaft rotated by a handwheel. By rotating the handwheel to suit, the front of the boiler could be raised when descending and lowered when ascending a hill. The centre of rotation of the boiler was, of course, the rear stub axles which acted as trunnions.

In Fig 16 we see details of what would now be called the chassis and three cross-sections through the outline arrangement. The chassis framing is very suggestive of railway locomotive frame practice and note the J decoration at the front end. Astheticism should never be denied!

Fig 17 gives details of the boiler and valve gear, the former containing no less than 48 tubes x 1¾in diameter, the barrel being exactly 3 feet in diameter.

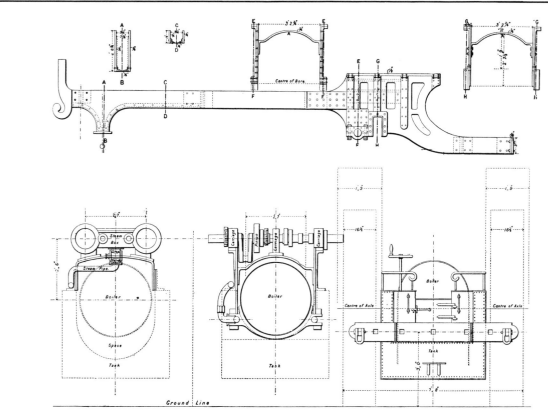

Fig 16 Frame and crankshaft details of the Burrell-Boydell engine.

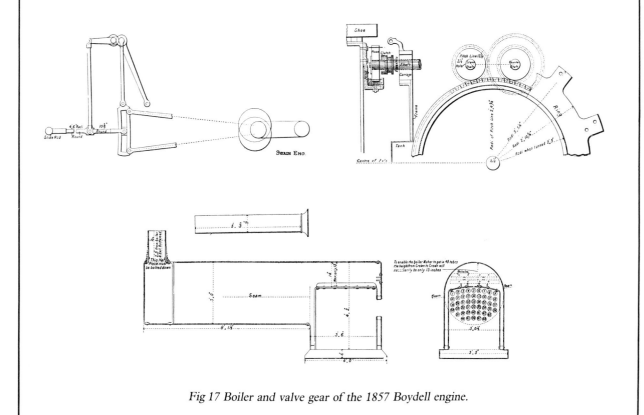

Fig 17 Boiler and valve gear of the 1857 Boydell engine.

Altogether an excellent example of boiler smithing at this period.

To make the clutch arrangement easier to follow, details are included in Fig 18 and in the lower view are given details of the feed pump, i.e. it was used to fill the main tanks with 600 gallons in 25 minutes and by changing the flow would feed the boiler. I have given many details as this engine was an historic machine and clearly laid the foundation for later and ingenious designs from the same drawing office. A noteworthy and original feature was the inclination of the boiler to suit negotiating hills. An almost identical engine for Brazil, sent away in 1860, is illustrated in Fig 19, seen attached to its road train which consisted of six or more trailers, a very paying load. The cost of such engines averaged £1,200.

Other modifications appeared in several engines for Venezuela completed at the end of 1859 and depicted in Fig 20, but here the duplex cylinders were 7in x 12in. From Fig 20 it will be seen that the rear portions are

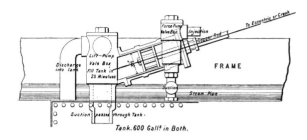

Fig 18 Pump and gearing details of the Boydell engine of 1857.

mounted on a pin either side of the firebox outer casing plates, the rear wheels being on the rear axle carried in the front ends of a lever either side, the fulcrum of these levers being the pins just mentioned. The rearmost ends of these levers were moved up and down by means of the handwheels and screw seen one on each side in the plan view. By lowering the boiler the crankshaft driving pinions would be lowered out of gear with the

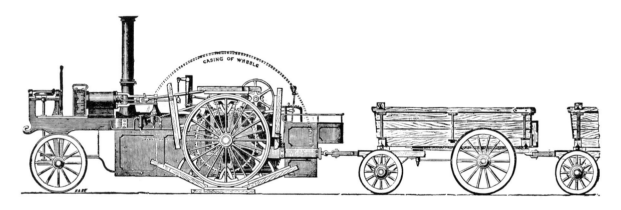

Fig 19 Burrell-Boydell engine made for Brazil.

Fig 20 A modified Boydell engine made in 1859.

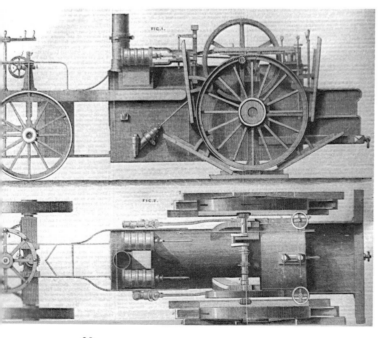

annular gears on the rear road wheels and by raising the boiler they would be engaged. This mechanism was obviously developed from the boiler inclination arrangement previously described and formed the subject of Charles I's Patent No 2701 of 1858.

In between designing and making these larger Boydell engines St. Nicholas Works produced a simpler "lightweight" version illustrated in Fig 21. It was evolved from what had become the firm's standard portable engine which was used as a basis and together with the 1856 engine is illustrated in Charles Burrell's first advertising sheet which may be dated c1860. This version had a single cylinder 7in x 12in, a single speed set of gearing incorporating a countershaft and it was horse steered. One of this class frequently travelled twenty miles a day drawing a threshing machine in the

Fig 21 The horse-steered Burrell engine with Boydell Patent Wheels.

wilds of Suffolk, forming perhaps the first example of the later familiar threshing engine drawing its "tackle" from farm to farm.

But why steer an engine by a horse? The reason was one of animal psychology. In these far-off days the traction engine was almost unheard of and such machines as were existing were pioneers. It was easy therefore for any horse meeting an engine to be frightened and to shy, but when confronted by one of their brothers they passed it without any fuss. Usually, when on strange roads, the horse was led by the "steersman" but when on familiar roads, our friend the horse showed his usual sagacity by leading the outfit home all by himself.

Here I think it opportune to illustrate the details of a typical shoe or pad as seen in Fig 22. Note the toe, the

Fig 22 Details of the shoes used with the Boydell wheels.

tread and the heel which approximate to the configuration of the human foot and were taken as a guide by Boydell. The length of rail on the shoe was necessarily equal to the radius of the driving wheel less clearance, the diameter of the wheel in these cases being 6 feet. The proportions of the toe had not to exceed one quarter of the length of the rail, whilst the length of the heel was found by experiment to be best when half the length of the toe.

James Boydell, the inventor, had been seriously ill shortly after the first engines, which worked successfully, had been built. He passed away at the end of June 1861. With a view to helping his widow and family, those interested in his patents formed The Endless Railway Traction Engine Company with a stated capital of £30,000 shares of £10 each, the Prospectus being issued in August 1861. What the response was is now unknown, but Charles I proved to be very interested and concerned. Other engines with Boydell wheels were made by Clayton, Shuttleworth & Co. of Lincoln, William Tuxford & Sons of Boston, Richard Garrett & Sons of Leiston, Richard Bach of Birmingham and E. T. Bellhouse of the Eagle Foundry, Manchester. Earlier, Boydell had formed a small company, Boydell & Glasier, whose works were in Camden Road, Camden Town, and this firm supplied many wheels to makers of heavy trolleys and wagons as well as some to the firms enumerated above.

The ultimate design of the Burrell-Boydell engine is depicted in Fig 23 which shows it to be a more compact design with integral front axle and steerage, large water tanks and all the motion gear neatly and compactly

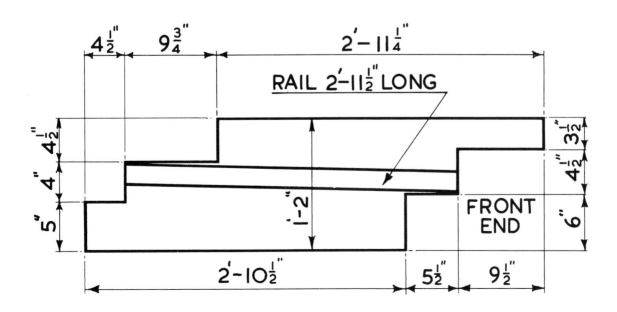

Fig 23 The famous Exhibition engine shown in 1862.

arranged. The subject of Fig 23 was exhibited at the International Exhibition in 1862 and its main dimensions are as follow:-

nhp	10
Cylinders, duplex	6½in x 12in
Cylinders, distance from centre of smokebox	2ft 3in
Firebox	2ft 5in deep x 2ft 9in wide x 2ft 5in high
Tubes, diameter	72 x 1¾in
Gear ratio	10 : 79
Weight in working order	7 ton 5 cwt
Average load	20 ton
Speed	4 mph

All gears were case-hardened and the valve gear was located between the cylinders with the four eccentrics in a nest between the cylinders. In this instance the driving wheels were of wrought iron having the rims, spokes and boss forged welded into one set piece, an example of real craftmanship. The links attached to the shoes worked through slots in the rim or face of the wheel and two rails were laid on each shoe instead of one, providing increased bearing surface. There was a polished copper cover for the safety valve and a polished copper flange or flare to the top of the tall

chimney, which was hinged at the base. This fine finish combined with workmanship of superior quality made the finished engine a delightful sight to behold.

Charles I, besides being an engineer, must have had a touch of the showman in his make-up because on September 12th 1862 he laid on a spectacular exhibition of haulage in Thetford in a field adjacent to St. Mary's Abbey. A corduroy road was improvised on the ploughed field of tree trunks laid side by side and over which the latest Burrell-Boydell engine hauled twenty tons in four low wagons with ease, many times. The wagons had plain wheels but the maker opined that had they been fitted with Boydell wheels the load might have been fifty tons.

After a capital lunch a general road test was carried out traversing the main streets of the town to the Common nigh unto the Castle Mound. Then the engine was detached, turned round in a very small circle and recoupled to the train to haul it through the Market Place and finally into Minstergate Street to the works. Many interested gentlemen attended representing business interests in Australia, New Zealand and, South America, Norway, Canada and Germany. What an interesting place Thetford was now becoming!

But ingenious as the Boydell wheel is in its conception, it was found in the hard school of practical use that, as could be expected, the shoes and pins wore rapidly, especially at any speed over 4 mph, causing their operation to become very noisy. So after the finely finished exhibition engine of 1862, no more such engines were made at Thetford.

In 1860 Charles Burrell had conceived the idea of producing a light self-moving road engine, incorporating many parts from the contemporary portable, springing the rear axle and using a pitch chain for the final drive as seen in Fig 24. Note the front steerage, very similar to that on the last Boydell, and the fine fluted chimney, an excellent example of the iron-founders craft and skill. The top flare was of polished copper. The driving sprocket could be clutched out of gear to give a neutral position for belt work. A stub countershaft carried the gearwheel-cum-sprocket combined, the drive from the crankshaft being taken by a small pinion engaging with the gear portion on the stub shaft. Such type of drive, in effect a three-shaft layout, demanded the cylinder to be at the rear end so it followed portable engine practice and was placed on the outer firebox crown plate. Two sizes were available viz. 8 and 10 nhp, the corresponding cylinder dimensions being 9in x 12in and 10in x 12in, the boiler being pressed to 100 psi in both cases. Incidentally, the engine in Fig 24 is that which was sent to and exhibited at the Great International Show at Hamburg in 1863 where it won for Charles I a First Class Great Silver Medal. After this success a small woodcut was prepared from the photograph in Fig 24 and which was used to illustrate Charles Burrell's advertisement in the *Norfolk Chronicle* from time to time during the latter part of 1863. It was perhaps the only instance of an illustrated traction engine advertisement appearing in a weekly newspaper.

Fig 24 A Burrell chain engine of 1860.

After three years experience, this first chain engine was modified into the workmanlike design depicted in Fig 25. Here the chain drive is now on both sides the countershaft running right across the engine. The

Fig 25 A later Burrell chain engine of c1865.

chimney is now hinged and another major change is that whereas in Fig 24 the smokebox is separate and riveted to the boiler shell, in the later example it is formed of an extension of the shell itself. Note the clutch lever operated by the steersman and not by the driver. With all these engines with front steerage a baffle plate was fitted to the smokebox door to protect the steersman from excessive heat. Two speeds were incorporated by making the gearwheel-cum-sprocket combination with different numbers of teeth, the sprockets both being of the same size, of course. High gear was on one side and low gear on the other. Very sharp corners could be negotiated by clutching the right or left road wheel into gear. The diagram in Fig 26 will explain the simple springing of the rear axle. A slot was cut in each front extension of the hornplates in which could slide up or down the axlebox A, made in halves, their motion being damped by the springs B. One must appreciate these springs had to withstand all the weight on the rear axle, about seven tons, as well as any road shocks. These springs were made of 1in square section steel with an outside diameter of 4¾in and a length of 7½in. They may be of interest to students of modern spring design and it is interesting to note that they were all produced, tempering included, in the works. In those days there were no specialist component suppliers as are available today.

What of the chains? Fig 27 illustrates a complete link as fitted to the chain engines of this period and they were in four sizes the pitch, P, being:–

3¹⁵⁄₁₆in for steerage chains
4⅞in for 8 hp traction engines up to 1875
6in for 12 hp ploughing engines
7³⁄₁₆in for 14 hp ploughing engines

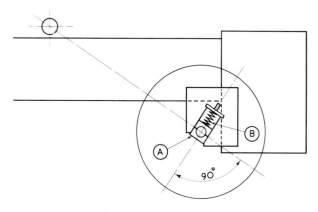

Fig 26 Diagram of the rear springing on the Burrell chain engine.

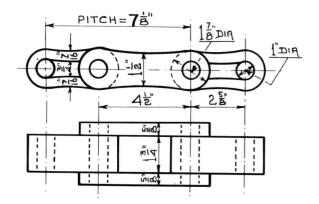

Fig 27 Chain details for Burrell chain driven road engines.

Fig 28 The Burrell chain drive ploughing engine.

The other dimensions were, of course, proportional to those in the diagram. Chains formed another accessory produced in the works which could not be bought out. Replacements were always in stock for any engine. With proper maintenance chains might last for years.

Another type of chain drive engine was the ploughing engine class. At first they were made under licence from John Fowler of Leeds but naturally boasted many Thetford features and thus we find Burrell characteristics in the typical crosshead guides, forked connecting rods, the arrangement of the cylinder blocks and the flare to the chimney top. In other words, the Burrell version of a Fowler engine and the first such built at Thetford is illustrated in Fig 28 and photographed in the field adjoining St. Mary's Abbey, the same field used for testing the Boydell engine mentioned previously. These early ploughing engines had duplex cylinders 7in x 12in and usually the clip winding drum was 5 feet in diameter. Note the very fine finish produced by the paintshop. The working pressure was

100 psi and the chain drive was on the left-hand side. Unlike the traction engines, the flywheel was on the right hand side, clearly shown in the part rear view included in Fig 29. Steering gear consisted of a large handwheel in the man-stand operating by a pinion and gear wheel, a short stub shaft below, this stub shaft being fitted with a sheave carrying a plain chain seen under the tender in Fig 29. Each end of the chain was connected to long eyed-links attached at their front ends to the front axle. I am told great strength was required to move the very wide front wheels if the ground be at all soft.

As the chain traction engines developed so was there parallel development of the ploughing engines and the next stage is shown in Fig 30 illustrating what was now called the long chain engine having the typical Burrell crosshead guide, but the cylinder is now at the front end with the barrel cast in one with a steam dome, thus forming a jacket. The remaining details will be clear

Fig 29 Another view of the engine in Fig 28.

Fig 30 Long chain drive Burrell ploughing engine.

from the illustration but with one unusual feature being the valve gear on the right-hand side, undoubtedly a relic of the Fowler influence.

Another modification to these ploughing engines was a shortening of the chain drive into the form seen in Fig 31. Although its general appearance is neater than the previous example, it has not the ruggedness of that in Fig 30. The illustration shows clearly the top run of the chain and the vertical shaft in the drum drive gear.

Fig 31 Short chain drive Burrell cultivating engine, No 729.

We come now to an unique form of Burrell chain engine which is shown in Fig 32 and which is an ancient photograph reproduced to illustrate this ingenious design. At this time Burrell practice was to use three shafts in the transmission but No 1061, the subject of Fig 32, had a fully elliptic spring each side above the rear axle with three intermediate driving shafts, the third carrying a differential beneath the boiler barrel, the chain drive permitting up and down movement of the rear axle. There were, of course, two chains, one each side. Two speeds were incorporated in the crank and second shafts giving ratios of $14 : 1$ and $23 \cdot 9 : 1$. *Oregon*, as it was named, left the works on December 5th 1883. Previous to this engine, the demand for chain engines had been relatively steady but then began to fall off so by 1880 the last chain engine proper to leave the works, No 858, was despatched on November 15th. However, and curiously enough, No 859 was sent off on August 27th that same year. Both were of 8 nhp, two speeds, spring mounted and complete with winding drum.

Fig 32 Special Burrell road engine named Oregon.

Although a chain drive facilitated springing the rear axle it cannot be denied that a precision component such as a pitch chain requires to be operated fully protected from dirt, wet, stones etc. and such detritus incidental to rural working, and under these conditions chain life was considerably shorter than if they had been enclosed. A parallel case is the anachronism of a

Fig 33 Charles Burrell's first all-geared traction engine.

pitch chain still used on some motorcycles where in bad conditions it runs in a mud bath. As in the case of chain traction engines, the motorcycle chain should have died a silent death years and years ago.

A man like Charles Burrell and his sons appreciated this and so we find as early as February 29th 1872 the first geared engine (as distinct from the Boydell engines) left the works and bore the number 532. It is seen in Fig 33 ready for exhibiting at Cardiff, Exeter, Bath and Dorchester Shows. Rated at 10 nhp it had a single cylinder 10in x 12in, and a flywheel with curved spokes 5 feet in diameter, all set on the boiler barrel of 2ft 9¾in diameter. Rear wheels were 5ft 6in diameter x 18in wide. Note the large belly tank and almost complete enclosure of the gearing in which were incorporated three speeds.

Simultaneously as No 532 was being designed (1871), the Thetford drawing office was heavily engaged on producing drawings for one of R. W. Thomson's "Patent Road Steamers" as they were termed, together with a special and unusual type of road engine, which being evolved only in this town were known as the "Thetford Engines". To deal with the Thomson Road Steamer first.

In Fig 34 is illustrated the first Thomson engine built at Thetford, numbered 491, and completed on February 1st 1871. Mounted on three wheels, the front served for steerage, movement of the axle being effected by the worm and wormwheel held by the steersman. The vertical boiler, for wood burning in this case, was

Fig 34 The first Thomson road steamer built by Charles Burrell.

Fig 35 Details of protective clips for solid rubber tyres.

placed just forward of the rear axle with the vertical engine having duplex cylinders 6in x 10in further to the rear, and geared to the rear axle with a countershaft embodying two speeds. These Thomson Road Steamers were renowned for their hauling capacity and seven were constructed in Thetford altogether.

It is not out of place to mention briefly that R. W. Thomson as a young man had been an engineer in the Dutch East Indies and as early as 1845 had achieved a Patent No 10990 of that year covering solid and pneumatic rubber tyres for vehicles. Little use was made of his pneumatic tyre partly because of the great difficulty he encountered in getting made wheels suitable for a pneumatic tyre. However, his idea embodying the solid type of tyre is illustrated in the upper view in Fig 35 where the tread of rubber 5in thick is protected by a series of iron treads pin-jointed together. Thomson has been generally very neglected but he is not forgotten as the following inscription on his birthplace in the market place in Stonehaven records:-

THE BIRTHPLACE OF
ROBERT WILLIAM THOMSON
THE INVENTOR OF THE PNEUMATIC TYRE
BORN 29th JUNE 1822
DIED 8th MARCH 1873

In his later years he was unfortunately a partial invalid suffering from *locomotor ataxia*.

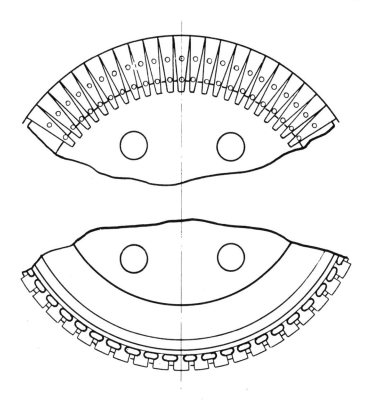

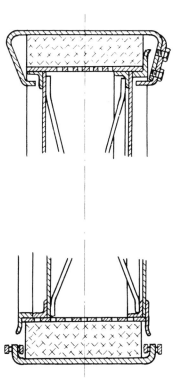

It was found in practice that the link pins were constantly breaking, for as to prevent the tyres getting out of place they had to be kept very tight. However, Charles Burrell I aided by George J. Fowell and in conjunction with Thomson, took out another joint Patent, No 3105 of November 16th 1871, where the tyre is protected by steel clips C, bent as seen but prevented from coming off by the master clip D fitted to the main clip by two set screws. Both clips C and D taper towards the wheel centre and all are perfectly free from one another and are outlined in the lower view in Fig 35. That these protected tyres really absorbed shocks and provide excellent grip is apparent by the driving wheels in Fig 34.

To consider now the special design of "Thetford Engine". A typical example is shown in Fig 36 which was a high-speed engine made for export to the Government of Crete and complete with its accompanying omnibus, also made in the works. Here the duplex cylinders are 7½in x 10in with a 12 nhp rating. The six feet diameter driving wheels were, of course, fitted with the Burrell-Fowell-Thomson patent treads, the work's number being 510. Note the twin front steering wheels.

Another excellent job was for the Russian Government and comprised a modified Thetford engine No 514 and mail van, both being made in the works. Named *Terimus* and rated at 8 nhp, the duplex

Fig 36 A Thetford engine and omnibus for Crete.

Fig 37 A Burrell engine for Russia with Mail Van.

cylinders were 6in x 10in and it is seen in Fig 37.

So far these special engines had the cylinders at the firebox end but a major departure was made in No 574 shown in Fig 38 and which was completed in May 1873 and exhibited at Hull and Bradford Shows. This was rated at 12 nhp with its pair of cylinders 7in x 12in fitted to the smokebox end of the barrel which was of 2ft 9in diameter and contained 62 x 1¾in diameter tubes. Driving wheels were of 5ft 10in diameter x 18in wide, but only iron shod in this instance. Note the front wheel, 3ft 7in in diameter, was thirteen inches wide and made up of two discs. The family are of the opinion that the driver-steersman in Fig 38 was probably Robert Burrell.

A slightly smaller example of these special Thetford engines is to be noted in Fig 39 depicting the final engine of this class. The excellent finish is easily apparent from the illustration where the driver is said to be George John Fowell, the co-patentee with Charles I and R. W. Thomson. Standing behind is the then machine shop foreman. The single front wheel was turned by worm and sector, each end of the short front axle being carried on four parallel coil springs with four

Fig 38 Burrell road engine No 574.

Fig 39 A special Thetford engine.

more smaller similar springs below acting as dampers, i.e. eight springs in all. The motion is enclosed in neat casing plates and other plates form the fuel bunkers on either side of the driver. An imposing air is given by the tall graceful stovepipe chimney. On occasions, these engines have reached 21 mph.

Besides being interested in wheel tyres, Thomson had designed and had made by several firms his patent Road Steamer where a vertical boiler was used with a two cylinder vertical engine and the complete arrangement is illustrated in Fig 40. The first made at Thetford was No 491 having duplex cylinders 6in x 10in driving the rear wheels through three shafts incorporating two speeds, all wheels having the Burrell-Thomson protected rubber treads. One of these road steamers, No 513, left the works on November 24th 1871 and after four years hard work was bought back in a part-exchange deal, overhauled and sold to the Harrogate Gas Company. Here it did so well that the Company purchased a new engine of later date.

Legislation imposed by minds limited and autochthonous at this period in history had, by the Locomotive Act of 1831, effectively killed the steam omnibuses of a previous decade by imposing stupid speed limits of up to 4 mph, usually compelling the herald with the red flag to exhibit himself in front. Thus

Fig 40 A fast road steamer from St. Nicholas Works.

Fig 41 Typical Burrell traction engine of this period, 1870–75, No 691.

the Thetford engines, for example, could not legally use their top speeds of up to 20 mph and therefore sales for such engines practically ceased. Another example of this senseless legislation concerned bridges. Under the later Locomotive Act of 1861 the owner of the engine was to be held responsible should his engine or its load fracture the bridge by traversing it. However no provision was made in any Act to apportion the blame should the load fracture a bridge when drawn by horses!

Consequently Charles I, aided by his sons, developed slower engines evolved from the first geared engine already noticed in Fig 33 and the first improved engine entirely re-designed is to be seen in Fig 41. Numbered 691, it was completed in April 1876 and was later exhibited at the Smithfield Show that year. Its single cylinder was 8in x 10in, now mounted on the smokebox end of the boiler which henceforth became the established and final position for all road engines made at Thetford. Driving wheels were 5ft 6in in diameter x 12in wide, the leading being 3ft 9in x 9in. The drive from the countershaft to the rear axle was by a pinion engaging with a gear on the axle and on the right-hand side. Such engines were designated as single-geared on the last motion. One the left-hand side

of the rear axle was mounted a winding drum with a differential on the countershaft, made in accordance with the firm's famous Patent No 4432 of 1876.

Considering now the ploughing engines; Fig 42 shows a typical example of a geared engine having a horizontal winding drum and a single cylinder 9in x 12in, the gear drive being on the right-hand side. The first of this design was No 766, despatched on June 3rd 1877 to a farmer in Ashill, Norfolk. The front axle was reversible so that it could be turned round to shorten the wheelbase if the winding drum were removed, when the engine could be used as an ordinary traction engine for belt driving.

As we have seen, the idiocy in the law relating to road transport had a stifling effect on the manufacture of road engines and so to survive, Charles Burrell and his sons set to and produced other types of engines for industry. Small horizontal engines had been available for some years and one is illustrated in Fig 43. With their large flywheels they were very steady running and were made in from 6 to 20 nhp sizes, the 6 nhp having a single cylinder 7¾in bore and the 20 nhp one of 18in bore, the intermediate sizes being proportional. Note

Fig 42 A geared Burrell ploughing engine.

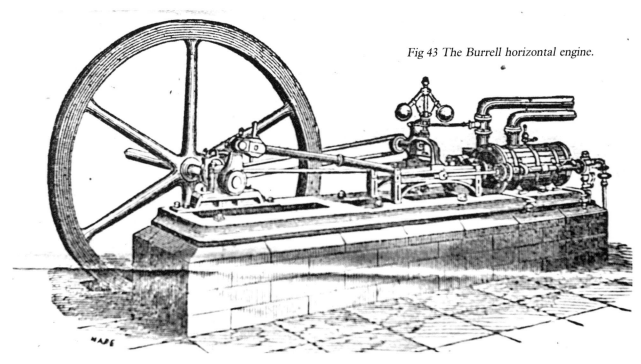

Fig 43 The Burrell horizontal engine.

the nicely-proportioned arched crosshead guides and the cylinder lagged with strip mahogany and polished.

Later, the design was improved and modified into the final form depicted in Fig 44 and made from 1889 onwards in powers from 8 to 20 nominal. The 8 nhp had a single cylinder 9½in x 12in increasing to 15in x 24in for the 20 nhp, the rpm being governed to suit requirements. All these engines could be fitted with an automatic expansion regulator viz. an expansion valve fitted on the back of the main slide valve and controlled by Frederick J. Burrell's governor made under his Patent No 5816 of 1882. Control of the engine was therefore by cut-off to suit the load and much more economical than by throttling the steam in the usual way at that time. One fine example of a 10 nhp, No 1393, was exhibited at the Smithfield Show in 1889 and was excellently received by the technical press of the period, which commented on its excellent design and finish.

Over the years the portable had not been neglected and in course of time embodied modifications and improvements which experience and progress suggested. Thus we find the second design took the form seen in the photograph in Fig 45. Judging by the great number of these engines made to order at this time it must have been a real "bread and butter" product. The smallest, of 1½ nhp, had a cylinder only 3¾in x 7in whereas the largest had one of 11½in x 14in and 100 psi was the usual working pressure. As the customer in those days was always right, he could have a compound engine if he desired, and these began at

Fig 44 Second design of horizontal engine by Charles Burrell.

8 nhp and on up to 20 nhp. In the former the cylinders were 6 in and 10in x 12in and in the largest size they were 9in and 14in x 16in. To suit some customers, a 12 nhp was available with duplex cylinders 8½in

34

Fig 45 The later design of Burrell portable engine, and threshing drum.

x 12in. The boilers were classic examples of the boilermaker's skill and craft and for the benefit of some model makers there is illustrated in Fig 46 the boiler for the little 1½ nhp engine. It was most compact and as will be seen its overall length was only 6ft 5¼in with a barrel of 1ft 8½in outside diameter.

There was a third design of the homely portable shown in Fig 47 which constituted the final form in which the finish of both paint and polished metal was second to none. The cylinder sizes and other main dimensions were approximately the same and to give further details a general arrangement drawing is

Fig 46 Diagram of the boiler for the 1½ nhp portable engine.

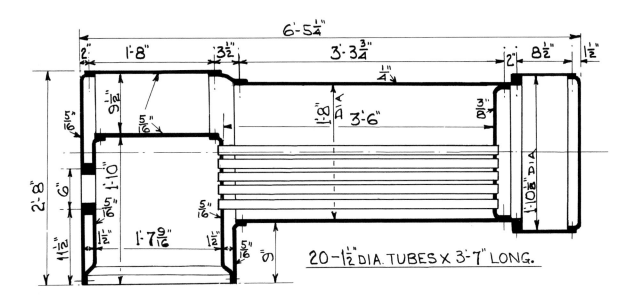

20-1½" DIA. TUBES × 3'-7" LONG.

Fig 47 (above) Final design of the Thetford portable engine.   Fig 48 (below) G. A. drawing of the last design of Burrell portable engines.

THETFORD CASTLE

included in Fig 48. The popularity of these utility engines can be judged from the fact that during the second half in 1873 no less than 82 portables, in addition to other types, were despatched from St. Nicholas Works, giving an average of about fourteen a month.

The semi-portable or overtype engine was merely a logical derivative from the true portable and the Thetford example is depicted in Fig 49. The base on which the firebox rested was water-filled to keep the ashpit cool and the front end was supported on a neat cast iron box and crown seen in the illustration. With their long, graceful connecting rods, these engines ran most smoothly. With a single cylinder they were made, of course, in the sames sizes as the ordinary portables; in fact they were merely portables without wheels.

What might be termed a second derivative from the portable is the undertype where the motion and valve gear is placed beneath the boiler, the lot being erected on a cast iron or girder-framed base, and an excellent example is shown in Fig 50. The great majority were compound engines bcause they were used entirely for driving workshops and other stationary machinery and therefore had to be able to start with the cranks in almost any position, not so easy with a single cylinder engine. In the odd cases where the HP crank was on a dead centre, the flywheel could be barred round, as necessary. These undertypes were available in no less than fourteen different powers of from 6 to 100 nhp and it is worth while to quote the cylinder dimensions as follow:–

nhp	6	8	10	12	14	16	20	25	30	40	50	60	80	100
HP bore	4¾	5½	6	7	7½	8	9	10	11	13	14	15	17	18
LP bore	8	9	10½	11¼	12½	13	14	16	17½	20½	22½	24½	28½	30
Stroke	10	12	12	14	14	16	16	18	18	24	24	27	30	36
rpm	220	180	180	165	165	145	145	130	130	100	100	85	80	80

Fig 49 Burrell's semi-portable or overtype.

Fig 50 The undertype engine from St. Nicholas Works.

Fig 51 Burrell's vertical high speed engine.

All dimensions are in inches, and the average ratio of piston areas will be found to be between 2·36 and 2·42 : 1. Apparently Italy was a good customer, for several were exported to that country. For many years two of these engines drove a flour mill in Norwich and in Water Orton and another a sawmill in Fakenham. Most were fitted with Burrell's Patent Governor controlling the cut-off by the expansion valve.

Here I think it is opportune to record that the first Burrell two-crank compound engine was the semi-portable No 1009, completed on December 7th 1886 having cylinders 7in and 12in x 14in. The cranks were at 90° and it preceded by some time the firm's patent single crank compound layout to be described later. This is worthy of note owing to the oft-repeated assertion that the first Burrell compound was of the single crank form.

Another product from Minstergate Street was the simple but robust vertical engine of which an example is to be seen in Fig 51. This proved to be a reliable prime mover as it drove part of the firm's turnery for some

Fig 52 Further details of the engine in Fig 51.

years. Number 1399, it had a single cylinder 9in x 10in and took steam at 100 psi. To augment the illustration in Fig 51 a cross-sectional and end view are included in Fig 52. Note the heavy flywheel and flange coupling. In this case governing was by the now popular Pickering type of instrument and in this application worked inverted. Altogether a most suitable subject for a model-maker.

The main dimensions were as follow:–

Cylinder	9in x 10in
Crankshaft diameter	3in
Valve ports	6in long
Flywheel	3ft 6in diameter x 7½in face
Overall height	5ft 3½in
Rotation	Outwards (overhand)
Governors	Pickering
bhp	45 on 120 psi

An unusual venture for a firm like Charles Burrell & Sons was small shipbuilding, where a small number of steam launches were fabricated in the boiler shop and then launched at an angle down the bank and into the Little Ouse River which flowed at the lower end of this shop. There is not a great deal of difference between working plates for a boiler or for a hull and this all helped to keep the boiler shop employed. A notable Burrell launch was that of the *Fenella* illustrated in Fig 53, which at one time was seen frequently on the River Yare plying from Norwich to Yarmouth and back. In many cases the shipbuilder contracted for engines to

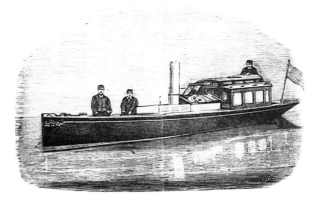

Fig 53 Burrell's steam launch Fenella.

Fig 54 The Burrell compound launch engine.

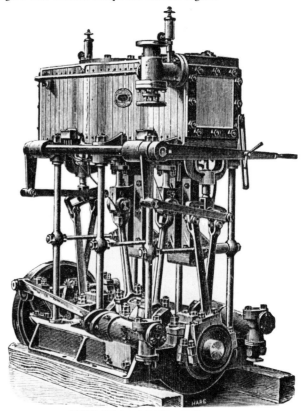

COMPOUND LAUNCH ENGINES

be built elsewhere but in these small Thetford boats the firm built the complete vessel including the engine and boiler. In the example of the *Fenella* it was powered by a beautifully-finished small compound engine No 1105 and the type is shown in Fig 54 where the cylinders were 4½in and 8½ x6in. All these little compounds worked condensing allied to a tubular surface condenser. Several sizes of launches were made viz. 35ft x 7ft, 35ft x 6ft x 3ft draught and a larger one 45ft x 7ft x 4ft draught. Some were most lavishly fitted-out with

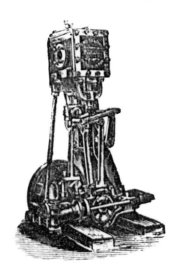

Fig 55 A single cylinder Burrell launch engine.

Fig 56 The pinnace boiler by Charles Burrell & Son.

cabins of American walnut and seats of polished teak, a tribute to the versatility of the pattern shop.

In addition to the compounds, a small single cylinder condensing or non-condensing engine for small tugs was available and a typical example is to be seen in Fig 55. The cylinder was 9in x 10in, the crankshaft running in two bearings as against three for the compounds. Where the vessel was liable to operate in salt water, a condenser could be supplied.

As in the case of the 1½ nhp portable boiler, the small marine boiler was also a work of boiler-making art and so the pinnace boiler is shown in Fig 56, which was suitable for a 2¼ hp pinnace, tug or launch engine. No less than 86 solid drawn brass tubes of 1¼in diameter were inveigled within the shell which was of only 2ft 6in diameter x 2ft 10in long. Some boilers of this type were supplied to other engine builders, incidentally. As many were used in Naval pinnaces, all were made to Admiralty Standards.

From small launches to large marine engines was not a very great step and therefore it is not surprising St. Nicholas Works entered the marine engine field with a nicely-proportioned engine to be seen in Fig 57 which was installed in a coaster, the *SS Mona*, in 1884. Rated at 300 ihp it had compound cylinders 20in and 40in x 24in turning the screw at 95 rpm and its list price was £1,100. The engine and boiler were fitted in King's Lynn Docks, the hull 100ft BP x 17ft 6in beam having been built by L. Smit & Zoon of Kinderdyk, Holland. In 1902 this ship was renamed *Fighting Cock* and in 1947

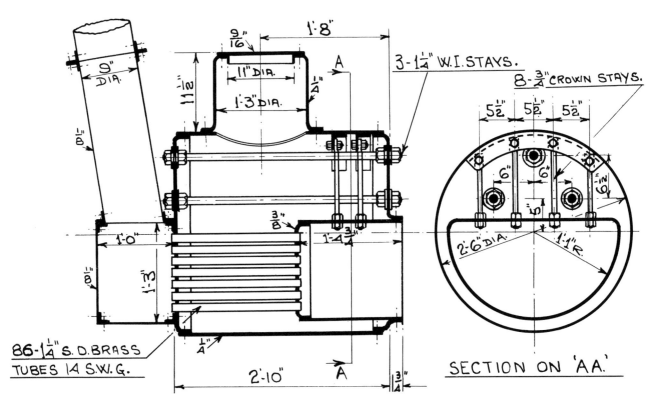

Fig 57 A large Burrell marine engine.

Fig 58 Another example of a Burrell marine engine.

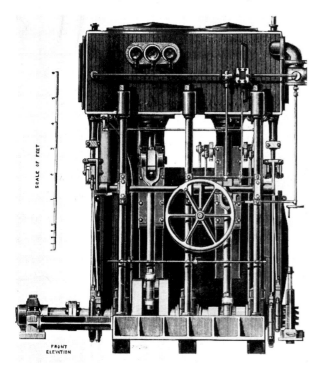

was again renamed *Trethosa* having been sold to the Fowey Tug Co. Ltd. The author enjoyed inspecting this grand Burrell engine as recently as 1950, when after

sixty six years of reliable service it had worn out two boilers!

An interesting side-light on valve setting. In the larger marine engines the HP lead on the downstroke was ³⁄₁₆in, and on the upstroke ½in; those for the LP being ⅛in and ½in respectively. In this way allowance was made for the weight of piston and rod acting against rotation on the upstrokes.

A further example of Norfolk steam engine building at its best is the 120 hp marine engine depicted in Fig 58 which was exhibited at the Naval and Submarine Exhibition of April 10th–20th 1882. Rated at 120 ihp the cylinders were 12½in and 22in x 18in, the engine turning over at 140 rpm.

When the transference of selected plant, machinery and engines in building and other records to the Garrett establishment at Leiston took place during 1929/30, unfortunately most of the records, illustrations and drawings of the more unusual and early Burrell engines which were of no commercial value to the new owners were either lost or deliberately destroyed. This accounts for why many details of all the various fixed and marine engines made at Thetford are lacking. The late Chief Accountant told me that at this period a pile of old drawings was burned in one of the work's yards including, he believed, all the original beautiful coloured drawings of the Boydell engines. Among the missing records are those appertaining to the steam tram engines produced in 1887. However, one general arrangement drawing drawn by none other than Frederick J. Burrell used to exist and it is from this lone sheet that I have prepared Fig 59 showing an outline of the engine. This engine was one of the few examples of Joy's valve gear embodied in a Thetford production.

Before proceeding further let us examine the "setting" for street steam tram engines in this "enlightened" period of Victorian history. The Red Flag vanguard Acts of 1861 and 1865 were, of course, still on the statute book but where tram engines were concerned there was a stipulation that required a most efficient brake gear and a governor which would apply the brake independently of the driver when 10 mph was reached. Freedom from mechanical and blast pipe noises was required and also from the emission of steam, hot air or smoke which might cause annoyance to the passengers. Steam trams had their antagonists like every other new mechanical invention of benefit of mankind and so we hear of horse-drawn tram men who would so manoeuvre their vehicles that a steam tram engine was sandwiched between two of them at a terminus. Now the feed on most of the tram engines was by pump operated off a main axle, functioning only when the engine was moving, so the worries of the driver concerning an overheated firebox crown can easily be imagined! Again there were not always recognised stopping places like we have today, and in this respect the anti-steam people scored heavily by requesting stops on the severest gradients where, out of a sense of decency, no horse-drawn vehicle would have been expected to stop. Imagine the re-start with, say, greasy rails and a governor cutting out if the slipping wheels exceeded the equivalent of 10 mph! To fulfil these conditions of service was the problem set the Thetford drawing office.

The important main dimensions appertaining to Fig 59 are as follows:-

Cylinders, compound	10in and 17½in x 14in inside the frames with HP by-pass valve to LP
Valves	On top of cylinders
Valve gear	Joy's
Diameter of coupled wheels	2ft 6in
Wheelbase	4ft 6in
Boiler	Loco type 20 nhp
Working pressure	160 psi
Feed valves	Sluice type

Weight in working order	12 tons
Gauge	3ft 6in
Tractive effort	12,890 lb working "double high" @ 83% cut off

How the valve gear evolved by the famous David Joy was applied to these engines is shown in the drawing reproduced in Fig 60 delineating a section through the LP cylinder and its valve chest. Note the rear end of the cylinder was cast integral with the barrel, a feature retained in most of the later engines. The gland box was detachable and bolted to the centre of the cylinder end. It will be noticed the reversing gear was duplicated, enabling the engine to be driven from either end. Another advantage of Joy's gear is its suitability for where the slide valves are on top of the cylinders as in this instance.

In Fig 61 we have details of the boiler where the barrel is 2ft 9½in inside diameter and four feet long between tubeplates. Ninety 1½in diameter brass tubes were coaxed into the firebox and front tube plates, both plates being ¾in thick, the firebox being of annealed copper. The very large dome served as an extra steam space as tram engines had to be worked at times on

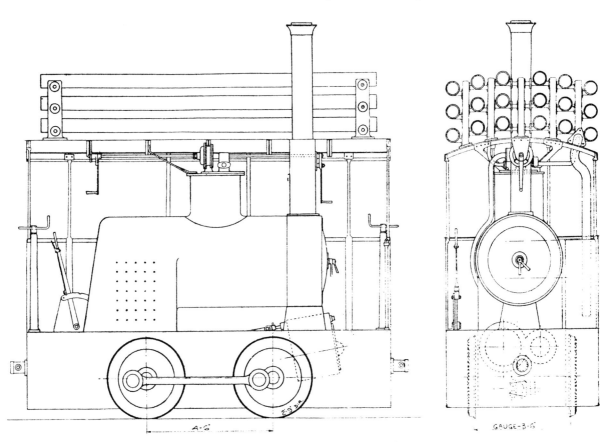

Fig 59 Burrell's compound steam tram engine.

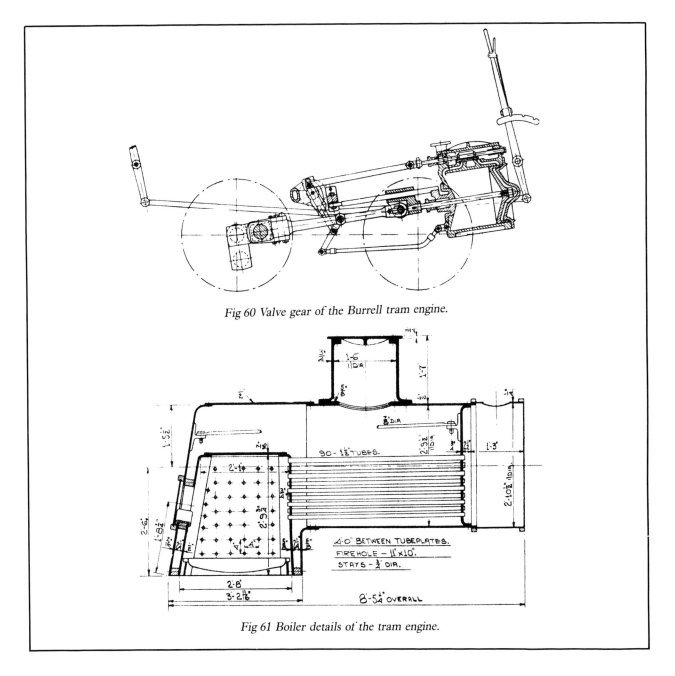

Fig 60 Valve gear of the Burrell tram engine.

Fig 61 Boiler details of the tram engine.

inclines with the barrel almost full of water. Shell and firebox casing plates were of Lowmoor iron or Siemans Martin Steel. As previously mentioned, the working pressure was 160 psi.

A most interesting item on these engines was the condenser made under Frederick J. Burrell's Patent No 14872 of 1887, and here it consisted of eighteen large copper tubes twelve feet long, nine being fixed each side of the engine roof. Within each tube was fitted another copper tube one inch less in diameter. The exhaust steam is led to enter the annular spaces between the eighteen pairs of tubes, condensation being effected by the motion of the engine through the air, causing a circulation of air currents through and over

them, this reducing the steam to hot water which was returned to the supply tank. Sometimes the feed tank became very hot because of this and the injector failed to function. It was then that the axle drive pump was used.

How the brakes came on when 10 mph or its equivalent in slipping axle speed of rotation was attained was a little complicated but very interesting, especially if compared with modern systems.

One brake block acted on the rear of each driving wheel, all four blocks being interconnected by two cross shafts and two side tie rods. The latter were attached to arms on a transverse shaft, one at each end of the chassis, the transverse shafts being turned by the action of the familiar handwheel and nut mounted one each end in the cab. To compensate, although each handwheel was rotated in the same direction for "on", the threads were right and left-hand so that the transverse shafts turned oppositely. Now in order that one brake wheel should not oppose the other, an amount of slack or lost motion – enough to allow the one actuated on at the moment to apply the shoes – was introduced on the wheel spindle by allowing the socket (through which the lower end of the wheel shaft passed), to move between two pins spaced a definite small distance apart on the shaft. The auto-brake gear comprised two steam brake cylinders placed one at each end of the engine, acting on an arm mounted on one of the two cross shafts already mentioned. They were so adjusted that in moving the shoes – only a fraction of an inch, of course, – on to the wheel tyre, the motion imparted failed to affect the hand-controlled links as it was accommodated for in the small amount of lost motion referred to. Control of the steam brake was made automatic in this manner. A countershaft was fitted in two bearings running right across the engine a little distance in front of the trailing axle and it was belt driven two to one up off the front axle. A centrifugal governor mounted on this countershaft, controlled by light link gear, very similar to that employed on a stationary engine, a small sensitive plunger relay valve on the side of the boiler barrel. This relay valve when opened passed high-pressure steam to the two brake cylinders. All that was necessary now was to adjust the governor so that at a speed equivalent to 10 mph of the driving wheels it just began to move the plunger of the relay valve when the brakes were just lightly applied, the intensity of application increasing rapidly for a very slight increase in speed causing more steam to be admitted to the brake cylinders. All very simple and out of the control of the driver who had only to ease each handbrake before starting. All this trouble and complication merely because of a Parliamentary whim imposing the 10 mph limit and for no logical reason. Things stay much as they were, parliamentarians show little pretence to intellectual eminence and still less to scholarship sublime!

Of the two engines made and supplied, the first went to the Bradford and Shelf Tramways and was numbered 6 by them. The other went to the Birmingham Central Tramways Ltd. (their No 71) and had a remarkable performance from the point of view of tractive effort. It worked on the Sparkbrook and King's Heath routes. It had no difficulty in dealing with the Bradford Street incline, 1 in 20 for 480 yards and the 1 in 18 incline on the King's Heath route. Neither of these could be rushed as in this instance there were definite stopping places at the bottom. On the Sparkbrook route it did 400 miles and 368 on the King's Heath. Later it

was transferred to the Small Heath line where the worst gradient was 1 in 18 for 640 yards, where it covered another 300 miles, bringing the total mileage to 1048. Fuel consumption was exceptionally good, the King's Heath route returning 6·4 lb. of coke per mile and the Small Heath route 8·7 lb. per mile. Water consumption worked out at 4·7 gallons per mile or 28·5 gallons per hour on the Small Heath line. The Sparkbrook route showed an even better return of about half the water consumption and much less coke. The high tractive effort was accomplished by fitting a three-way valve to the valve chests so that both cylinders could be worked high pressure for short periods, often when starting. In this way a larger load could be started than by any other non-compound engine of the same size. Assuming 85% boiler pressure on the pistons the calculated tractive effort when working "double high" would be 12,890 lb.

Fortunately an old engraving of one of these tram engines and its car has only recently been discovered by the author, showing how it appeared to the prospective passenger, and it is illustrated in Fig 62. A most excellent look-out was afforded the driver by extensively glazing the surrounds of the engine, there being six panels on either side with three each end, eighteen glazed panels altogether. It is an unbounded field for speculation how such engines (considering all makes as a type) might have developed had Parliament been wise.

One of the most spectacular as well as ingenious productions from St. Nicholas Works was the roundabout depicted from an old photograph in Fig 63. Its great peculiarity was that it consisted of two rotating portions – an inner and an outer. The inner took the form of a small locomotive which drew several small gondola-like carriages behind it, all on a circular track and it ran counter-clockwise. By suitable gearing arranged around the centre-pin it drove the outer portion consisting of a three-abreast set of gallopers clockwise. The railway track was on a slight raised platform and the whole creation was entirely novel. It was a beautiful piece of work made to the order of the Locomotive Merry-Go-Round Co. Ltd., the fine organ and galloping horses being made by a midlands firm. In Fig 63 the set is shown erected for testing in the work's yard and the gentleman in a bowler hat and seated on a horse nearest the camera was Robert Burrell, who was Works Manager at this time. The locals were entertained free of charge in this instance, the year being 1890. Later, it was erected in the Market Place, where patrons then had to pay a modest 2d per ride. Even so, it is on record that the first day's takings were £100!

During this period of miscellaneous activity the road engine proper had not been neglected and so by c1890 the fine-looking single cylinder two-speed traction

Fig 62 (above) Engraving of the Burrell tram engine attached to its car.

Fig 63 (below) The famous Burrell duo-directional roundabout.

engine took the form to be seen in Fig 64. Usually they were available in three common sizes viz. 6, 7 and 8 nhp the cylinders being respectively 8in x 10in, 8½in x 12in and 9in x 12in, the working pressure being 140 psi. Rear wheels were 5ft 9½in for the 6 and 7 nhp, those for the 8 nhp being 6ft 6in.

These engines could be made with compound cylinders, the dimensions for the three sizes being respectively 5½in and 9in x 10in, 6¼in and 10½in x 12in and 6½in and 11in x 12in, the remainder of the specification being as for the single cylinder machines. A typical two-crank compound engine is to be seen in

Fig 64 Burrell single cylinder traction engine of 1890.

Fig 65 The compound Burrell engine typical of this later period, No 2984.

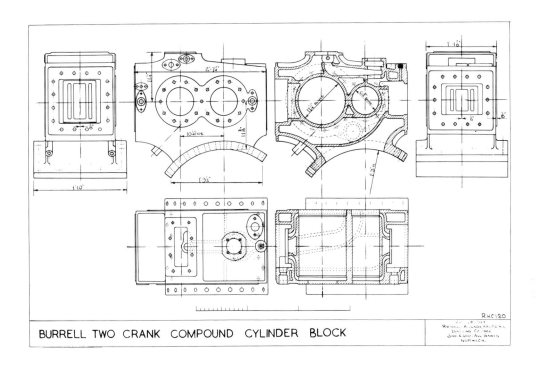

BURRELL TWO CRANK COMPOUND CYLINDER BLOCK

Fig 66 Cylinder block details for a Burrell road locomotive.

Fig 67 Arrangement of Frederick Burrell's patent cylinder block.

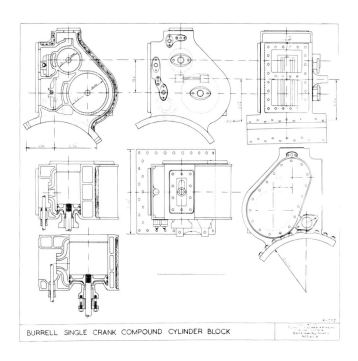

BURRELL SINGLE CRANK COMPOUND CYLINDER BLOCK

Fig 65 and today many engines of this design are to be seen at steam assemblies. The design of the cylinder block was perhaps the neatest of any English traction engine and worthy of examination which may be made from the drawing included in Fig 66. This shows the 8 nhp block which was fitted to all later showman's road locomotives of this rating.

At this period in agricultural history the humble traction engine was slowly gaining favour with the farming fraternity but they wisely, perhaps, preferred simplicity so that the simpler the design the more acceptable it would be. To simplify the two-crank compound design was Frederick John Burrell's object embodied in his famous patent No 3489 of 27th February 1889 and a general arrangement drawing of the mechanism is depicted in Fig 67. Note particularly the cylinders are arranged one over the other diagonally, the high pressure always being on top. Both pistons reciprocate together, i.e. they begin and finish each stroke at the same moment, the ends of the piston rods being cottered into one large crosshead usually no less than twelve inches long. A stout connecting rod transmits the power to the single throw crankshaft. Obviously, and like the pistons, the two slide valves must move together so their rods are yoked to a common head, the primary rod being connected to the die-block in the usual way. The rest of the valve gear was Burrell standard practice.

Both valves chests are separated by a horizontal fillet, the exhaust port of the high pressure chest exhausting direct into the low pressure chest and the low pressure exhaust progressing to atmosphere in the usual way up the chimney. Note that both valve chests are sealed by a common cover fixed by sixteen or more Whitworth studs and nuts bearing the famous nameplate and work's number.

Further details of this arrangement when embodied in a production engine are to be seen in Fig 68, where the mechanism is shown very clearly and should be studied in conjunction with the drawings in Fig 67. Exhaustive tests were carried out on the prototype No 1290 of 8 nhp which, of course, included brake tests and the simultaneous taking of indicator diagrams. These diagrams are reproduced in Fig 69 where in diagrams (a) the lever was in the third notch, the boiler pressure 160 psi, the indicator spring being 100 and the output 64 ihp. As the corresponding brake horsepower was 58 this gives an excellent figure of 90·6% mechanical efficiency effected by a combination of accuracy in erection and fitting and as will be seen from the diagrams, an extremely small pressure drop

Fig 68 (facing page) Further details of the single crank compound system.

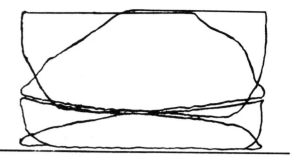

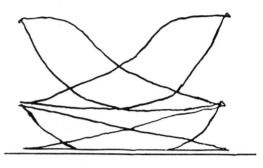

Fig 69 Indicator diagrams from the single crank compound cylinders.

between the HP exhaust and LP inlet pressures. In other words the thermal cycle was extremely good. Fig 69 (b) shows diagrams on a lighter load with the lever in the first notch, where again the pressure drop is minimal. Further tests returned the excellent figures of 80 ihp at 200 rpm with the safety valves lifting at 160 psi. The heating surface was 150 sq ft and the ihp of 80 represents 1 ihp per 1·875 sq ft of heating surface. This accounts for a day's threshing being done on only 3½ cwt of best steam coal.

Charles Burrell & Sons built a number of Universal Ploughing Engines utilising their single crank compound system and Fig 70 illustrates both this type of engine with the winding drum on the side together with the Patent compounding, looking on the nearside. The firm always favoured the three shaft transmission layout although there were few exceptions as in the case of Fig 70 where the low speed pinion can be seen on the second shaft through the flywheel spokes.

Over the years the humble portable had not been neglected and some were produced having the single crank compound arrangement of cylinders and an excellent example is shown in Fig 71. Note the fine finish of both motion and paintwork.

The capacity of an engine to do useful work depends upon a boiler capable of supplying sufficient steam and all later Burrell boilers were good steamers. A typical boiler for an 8 nhp engine is included in Fig 72. Note the smokebox is separate to the shell and secured by rivets through both the box and an extension of the

Fig 70 (above) Universal ploughing engine with patent compound cylinders.

Fig 71 (below) A single crank compound portable.

shell, with a packing ring between them. When a smokebox had to be removed it could be done by drilling out the ring of rivets and with no detriment to the shell plate. An important point, as the shell plate is part of a pressure vessel. The rest of the design is evident from the drawing.

A back axle section or a section through the shafts of a three-shaft traction engine or road locomotive may be

of help and interest to some owners of Thetford-built engines as well as to the model maker and consequently such a section of a double crank compound engine is shown Fig 73. This design incorporates several famous Burrell patents. Firstly, the arrangement of the clutch gear covered by Patent No 2881 of 19th July 1878 and applicable to an engine with both two and three speeds. Secondly, the method of quickly locking the

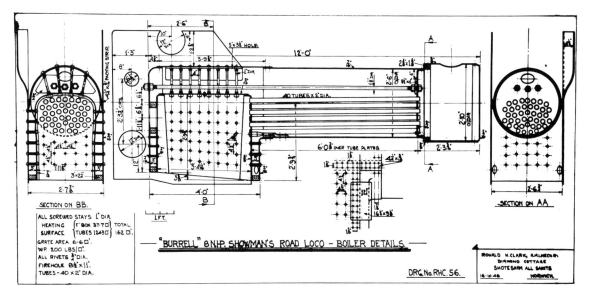

Fig 72 Boiler drawing for the Burrell 8 nhp road locomotive.

Fig 73 Back axle section of the double crank compound road locomotive.

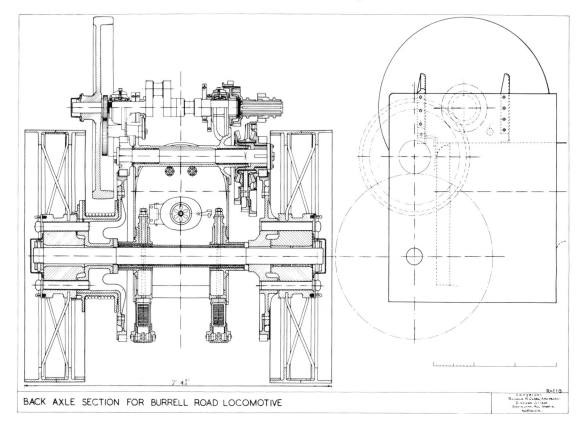

BACK AXLE SECTION FOR BURRELL ROAD LOCOMOTIVE

differential so that in an awkward situation the drive became solid and fixed. This was embodied in Patent No 24978 of 1905.

Here it may be appropriate to mention briefly the clutch and change speed mechanisms just noted. In Fig 74 the upper drawing shows the two-speed gear layout where in the fast speed pinion A on the crankshaft is placed inside and recessed over the bearing, the slow speed pinion B being placed outside it. The two pinions are held laterally by forks C and D which fit into grooves turned in the bosses of the pinions, the other ends of the forks sliding on a round bar E which is attached to a bracket K mounted on the side plate P. The forks have projections T and U on the sliding forks C and D respectively, thus holding either of them stationary. A lever H having one end working on a pin on the fork C and the middle on a pin on the fork D is used for sliding the pinions in and out of gear, the action being as follows:– With the mechanism shown in the position in Fig 74 both pinions are out of gear and the locking plate F is holding the fork C and consequently the pinion A. On withdrawing the pin W the lever H can be moved to N, thus moving the fork D and its pinion B into gear, the fork C (being held stationary of course by F), the pin on it acting during this movement as a fulcrum to the lever H. If, however, on the other hand it is desired to put the pinion A into gear, the locking plate F must be pulled back by V when the other end of it will engage with U and hold the fork D and with it its pinion B stationary, and so out of gear. In this instance the pin Y on the fork D acts as fulcrum to the lever H which can then be moved to O, thus sliding the fork C, and with it its pinion A, into gear. It will be noticed that both pinions cannot be placed into gear at the same time as the plate F is so arranged as to lock one fast while the other is free to be moved. Both pinions slide on the multi-splined end of the crankshaft.

The third speed gear was developed for the faster showman's engines and road locomotives and is shown in the lower diagram in Fig 74 where G is the top speed pinion and J the top speed gear on the spur ring. Meshing of G with J is effected by moving G along its splined centre on to the outside of which it is recessed to receive, by the lever Z. Note particularly that until the second speed part just described in the preceding paragraph is shifted and pinned into neutral, the lever Z cannot be moved.

A natural development from the road haulage engine is the steam roller and St. Nicholas Works were producing rollers as early as 1891 when the first, No 1535, left the works in December that year. It had a single crank compound cylinder block and was unusual in having four shafts in the transmission. Two Burrell patents appertained to road rollers, the first being

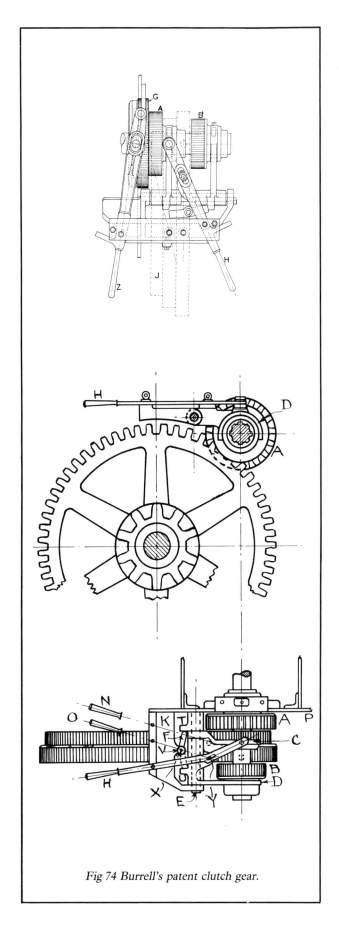

Fig 74 Burrell's patent clutch gear.

Patent No 8017 of 29th April 1893 by Frederick J. Burrell and comprised the front roller fork illustrated in Fig 75, applied to all subsequent machines. The invention consists of the centre pivot A and B is the front fork carrying the axle for the two front rolls. A special collar C formed with two upper curved cheeks fitted around the base of the pivot A, these curved cheeks mating into receiving curves formed in the cast iron saddle head of the roller. A upper bearing D is fitted to the top of the pivot A on which A can turn as the rolls are steered, the bearing D being located in the top of the saddle. The action is quite simple and such that as the rolls rise from side to side they can oscillate by virtue for the curved cheeks on the collar C moving in the corresponding curves in the saddle. At the same time the pivot A can rotate according to the steerage applied to the front rolls via the fork by the chains.

The second Patent was No 15926 of 18th July 1896 in the joint names of Frederick J. Burrell and Harold Frederick Rutty and covers a scarifier which could be fitted to any Thetford-built roller. This scarifier and the patent roller front fork bearing are both incorporated in the fine engine depicted in Fig 76. It will be observed that the scarifier would work in either direction; no

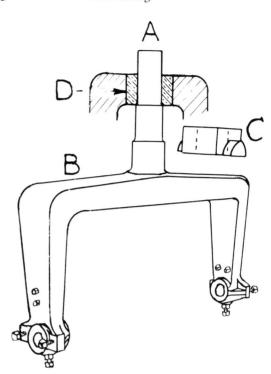

Fig 75 Patent roller fork bearing.

Fig 76 The Burrell-Rutty scarifier incorporated on a roller.

scarified surface was rolled after it had been done and no stresses were imposed upon the tender of the engine as the scarifier is fitted direct on to the rear axle. Instead of hand operation as shown, a steam or hydraulic cylinder could be fitted, but the majority of those made had manual operation. H. F. Rutty was a contractor in Ilford and by an agreement dated 28th December 1896 the works agreed to pay him 10% royalty of the catalogue price for each roller sold using this scarifier.

Charm is difficult to define. It is possessed sometimes by some ladies and some gentlemen. It can be possessed too by certain mechanisms and machines where the charm is at once obvious to the eye of the sympathetic beholder. It is the author's opinion that the double crank compound roller illustrated in Fig 77 has beauty inherent in its excellent lines and proportions. Naturally it is not given to everyone to appreciate traction engine and road roller beauty.

If a customer so desired he could have any size and

"THE BURRELL"
SPECIAL 8 TON ROAD ROLLER.

Fig 77 A late and very good-looking compound Burrell road roller.

Fig 78 Burrell's first design of steam tractor.

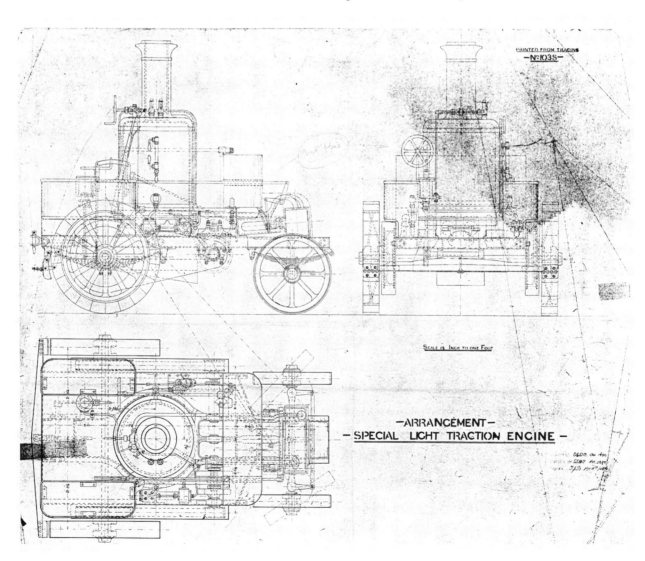

—ARRANGEMENT—
— SPECIAL LIGHT TRACTION ENGINE —

weight of roller fitted with single crank compound cylinders when the lines would be similar to Fig 77, excepting the slightly different outline of the cylinder block.

Until the Heavy Motor Car Act of 1903, steam road engines were limited to 4 mph and had to be in charge of a driver accompanied by a steersman. The 1903 Act, rather reluctantly one feels, graciously permitted light road engines to travel at 5 mph and under the control of only one man, the driver. But the weight was not to exceed five tons unladen. The trade were quick to take advantage of these belated concessions and so it was not long before Steam Motor Tractors as they were termed, were being made by several leading firms. Charles Burrell II and his staff had been investigating the practicability of such light engines some years previously and it was a little prior to 1900 that a small one-off experimental special was produced. It is illustrated by the line diagram in Fig 78 prepared by the author from a torn and tattered original, fortunately preserved. The engine appears to be a small one of 4 nhp with the peculiar feature (for a Burrell product) of trunk crosshead guides. The countershaft is placed immediately below the crankshaft and gears to constitute two speeds were arranged. Final drive to the

back axle was by roller pitch chain. Semi-elliptical springs were fitted above each wheel and the driving wheels were fitted with patent wood blocks. Braking was by a steam brake activating a brake block on each rear wheel. Steam was supplied from a vertical multitubular quick steaming boiler similar to that seen in Fig 85. Ackerman-type steerage was used, the smaller front wheels being iron-shod. Water was carried in the front tank above the cylinders and fuel in the side panniers mounted aft. Popular rumour has it that this interesting engine was often used to haul loads to and from the works and the station yard and for other local journeys, but no further details of it or what became of it are to be found.

With the accumulated experience of many years of road locomotive design for guidance, the Thetford drawing office was not long in preparing a workmanlike and pleasing design of tractor depicted in Fig 79 bearing the work's No 2787 which was completed in the shops on 18th December 1905. Early in the new year, 1906, it was thoroughly tested up Croxton Hill and used for all manner of haulage jobs. In fact it was the work's "Demonstration Model" for three years, being

Fig 79 The Burrell single cylinder light tractor of 1905.

Fig 80 Burrell's double crank compound steam motor tractor.

Fig 81 The famous Burrell Gold Medal tractor.

ultimately sold on 8th March 1909. The second made, and to a definite order, was No 2797, despatched on 20th January 1906, and also with a single cylinder.

For a lightweight engine to move a respectable load suggested compound cylinders and therefore the third tractor, No 2802, had double crank compound cylinders 5in and 8½in x 9in, taking steam at 200 psi. A side view of one of this type is shown in Fig 80. A valve for admitting high pressure steam, sometimes for starting, to the low pressure valve chest was a standard fitting on all the compound tractors which later ones were all of the two-crank compound form.

As in the case of their larger brethren many were sold to showmen where they were much liked. In 1908, the RAC decided the stage its Tractor Trials. Charles II decided to enter an engine and so No 2932 was unstintingly prepared and carried a very high class finish as may be seen from the view in Fig 81. The start of the Trial was on 9th September 1908 and it lasted for 22 days during which time the engine covered 686 miles and used 56¼ hundredweights of coal and 420 pounds of wood, the coal consumption working out 9 · 2 pounds per mile. The lubricating oil used totalled 50 pints. It drew a load of 6 tons gross behind the drawbar and time lost due to stoppages other than those caused by traffic conditions or which were compulsory was 4 hours 6 minutes.

The judges highly commended the machine for accessibility, adequacy of platform area, adhesion, brakes, condition after trial, finish and workmanship, freedom from smoke, general appearance, hill climbing, quiet running and steering gear. In addition they also commended it for cleanliness. They unhesitatingly awarded it the only Gold Medal given in the Trial and so for ever afterwards this Burrell product was known as the Gold Medal Tractor.

In competitions like this Trial very much depends upon the human element and wisely the firm employed one of their regular demonstration drivers, Harry Parlett, accompanied by two reserve drivers, Harry Clark and Frank Miller.

A trial lasting twenty two days showed that at this period they didn't stint themselves – they did things very well!

A typical showman's tractor is included Fig 82 which illustrates the gentle lines of these charming little engines.

The law eased somewhat after World War One and permitted steam motor tractors to weigh up to 7½ tons unladen and still to be in charge of only one man. The legislators of that time no doubt thought themselves very brave but what of today with one man in charge of thirty or more tons at more or less express speeds?

The first larger tractor was No 3951, exhibited at the Newcastle-Upon-Tyne Show in 1923. It was very

Fig 82 A Burrell showman's tractor.

similar in outline as will be seen from Fig 83 but the cylinders were naturally slightly larger being 5in and 8½in x 9in.

As long ago as 1900 the drawing office had been devoting some time to a design of steam wagon and during the next year there emerged from St. Nicholas Works a steam wagon or "lurry". Although no photograph or engraving of this original ingenious design has come to light, a torn and damaged contemporary line drawing has survived from which the illustration in Fig 84 has been prepared. As will be seen, the compound engine was of the undertype form having cylinders 5½in and 9in x 6in, using steam at 200 psi from a vertical boiler with a barrel outside diameter of 2ft 2in containing 170 cross tubes ⅞in diameter. Its overall height was only 4ft 3in. Two speeds were provided on the countershaft, the final drive being by double inverted-type tooth chains and gear changing was effected by sliding both crankshaft pinions to suit. Although little more is known about this interesting and pioneer vehicle, the late Herbert Burrell told me it was used very extensively as a general carrier about the work's yard and additionally performed other transport jobs for local people. Apparently much was learned from these experiences.

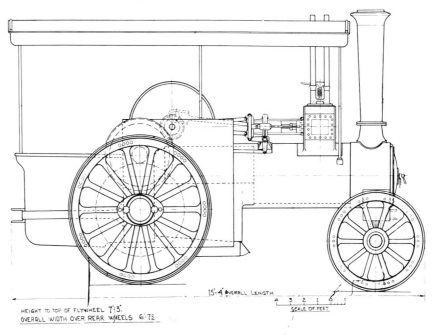

Fig 83 The 7½ ton Burrell compound tractor.

Fig 84 The first Burrell wagon of 1901.

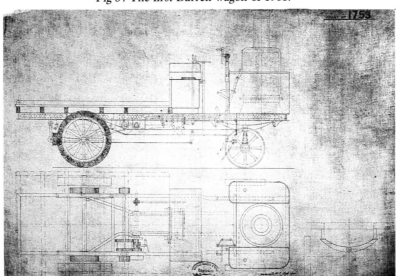

A diagram of the interesting boiler is shown in Fig 85 from which one should note that the shell, uptake and crown plates were no less than ¾in thick. There were bolted flanged connections securing the crown plate to the uptake and also the shell to the taper skirt. In this way the boiler could be dismantled for cleaning and any necessary attention to the tubes.

During the first ten years of this century the Thetford drawing office and works were extremely busy on all types of traction engines and an amount of separate boiler work, together with certain work for the Admiralty. This accounts for why it was not unti 1911 that the first conventional type of wagon was completed and which bore the number 3276. It was superbly finished and was exhibited at the Royal Norfolk Show that year which was held on a large pasture close by Thetford Bridge Station. It is said that it was towed to the Showground so that no oil spots or other obnoxious matter would mar the superlative efforts of the paintshop! Fig 86 illustrates one of this series where the differential was on the countershaft, the drive to the back axle being taken by twin roller pitch chains, one each side. Of course two-crank compound cylinders were used in every wagon, the cylinders being 4⅛in and 7in x 7½in, taking steam at 200 psi as in the Gold Medal Tractors. It is interesting to note that tractors and wagons at this period were using steam at this

Fig 86 Side view of the Burrell two-chain wagon.

pressure whereas railway locomotive pressures were usually at 175 and occasionally 180 psi.

To make the arrangement of twin chains quite clear, the view in Fig 87 shows how they were placed, with one outside of the framing each side. The rear axle was dead with only the wheels rotating on it. The differential, as we have noted, was on the counter-shaft.

Fig 87 View on the twin rear chains.

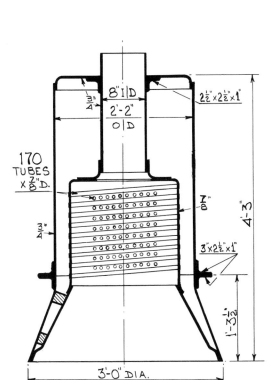

Fig 85 The boiler for the first wagon.

Fig 88 The single chain wagon.

Experience showed that some customers and users would overload a wagon imposing extra stresses, especially on the countershaft, and several were known to break therefore. The drawing office solved the problem by using only one chain (which was lighter than two) and incorporating the differential inside the sprocket on the rear axle, which was now, of course, "live", and most of the following and later vehicles were of the single chain type. One, No 3883, is depicted in Fig 88 and the first of this type was No 3394 completed on 19th August 1912, the year of the Great Norfolk Flood.

Here I think it is opportune to remark that one or two of the early overtype wagons had an annulus or internal gear drive in the rear wheels, but this design was not adhered to for long on account of damage to the

Fig 89 A double crank compound Burrell tipping wagon to carry six tons.

gear teeth by dirt, stones and other objects.

The last new design of any vehicle produced was the larger 6T wagon, an example of which is included in Fig 89, the first made being No 3953, completed on 13th December 1924 for a customer in Mannerston. Another 6T wagon, No 4068, for a customer in Bishop's Lydeard, was sent away resplendent in a rich royal blue. To provide that little extra urge for a 6T load, the boiler was designed for a pressure of 220 psi.

The wagon boiler was a choice example of the boilermaker's craft and skill and worthy I feel of an illustration which may be seen in Fig 90 giving all the important dimensions. As a fitting conclusion to these notes on the Thetford steam wagons I must record an occasion when once I trailed a Burrell wagon in Suffolk. At times when conditions allowed, the speedometer of my Brough Superior indicated 25 mph! This was the equivalent of about 900 rpm of the compound engine, very good for an engine with slide valves.

Like many other concerns, Charles Burrell & Sons designed and made a fair number of special or non-standard engines – specials we may call them, although some of these designs were never translated into a complete machine. The special wagon in Fig 91 is a very good example of an advanced design and was estimated for in 1924. The engine, chassis and body follow orthodox practice but the great interest lies in the transmission. A roller pitch chain each side takes the primary drive from the crankshaft to a countershaft placed and across the footplate, and mounted on the countershaft is a bevel pinion meshing with a similar wheel on the forward end of a four-speed heavyweight gearbox, the final drive from this box to the back axle being via an enclosed propellor shaft and robust

Fig 90 Drawing of the high pressure wagon boiler.

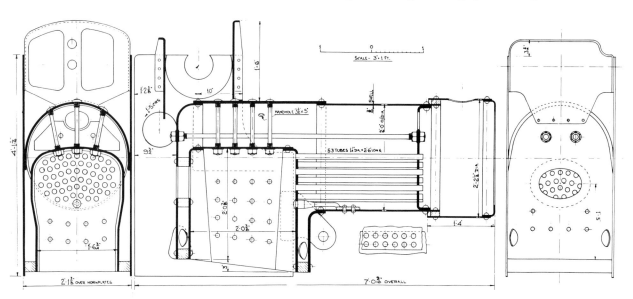

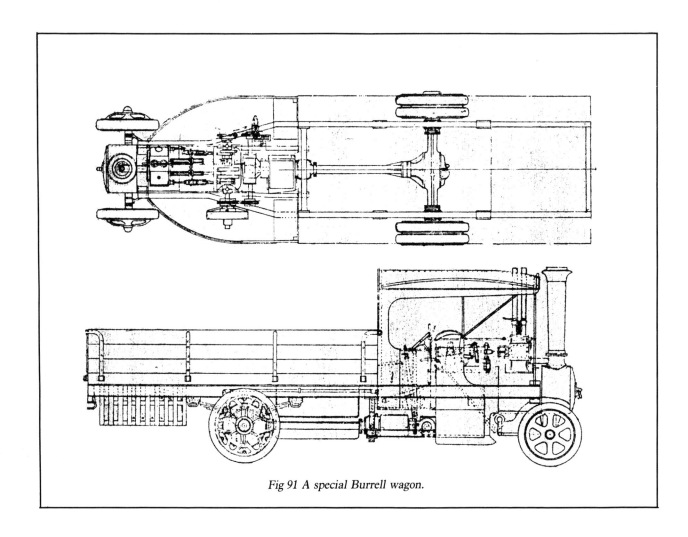

Fig 91 A special Burrell wagon.

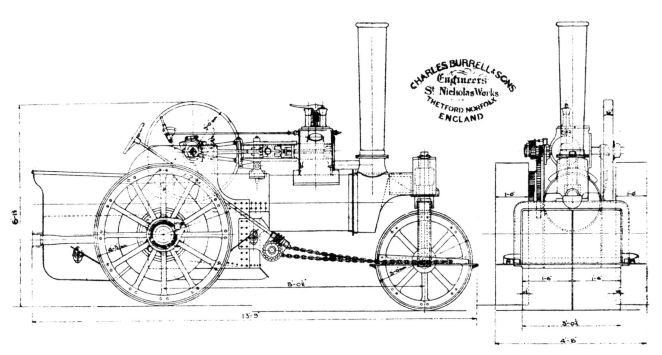

Fig 92 Burrell's small 3 ton single cylinder roller.

differential. Gear change was by hand lever and gate and, due to the steam engine being quickly reversible, the wagon had therefore four forward, four reverse speeds and a neutral position. No clutch had to be provided for and when changing from one ratio to another the throttle would be momentarily closed or eased. Coal was carried in two bunkers, one beneath the driving seat and the other at the rear and slung under the body. The water tank was suspended beneath the forward part of the body and saddled the propellor shaft casing. Twin rear and single front wheels shod with solid rubber Pirelli tyres completed the main specification, the remaining details of which followed the firm's usual wagon practice. It was a pity such an interesting machine was never built as four speeds combined with the flexibility of the steam engine would have made its navigation a sheer delight.

Reverting back to rollers there was the diminutive little 3T machine seen in the elevation and front end view in Fig 92. It was intended for rolling wide paths, narrow lanes, forecourts and so on but although estimated for, apparently an order never matured. As will be noted, it was only of 13ft 9in overall length, 4ft 8in overall width and the single cylinder would have been only 5½in x 8in.

If an extra or special fitting constitutes a special engine, then all crane engines could be termed specials and a typical crane engine is to be seen in Fig 93. The rope winding drum was fitted on the front of the smokebox driven by a wormwheel on its nearside end, the worm itself being on the end of a longitudinal shaft bevel driven off the crankshaft. There was, of course, a dog clutch to move the shaft bevel along the shaft and so out of mesh. These cranes would lift from four to five tons. A crane engine was a most handy tool as the writer can testify, having used them on more than one occasion. In their large and lavish catalogue the makers said "*We have had one in constant use for twenty seven years in our works, and would not be without it on any account. The engine does all the lifting about our yards, etc. etc.*"

Fig 93 A fine compound crane road locomotive.

Fig 94 The special Colonial Burrell traction engine.

Specials were manufactured for countries where straw and grasses were surplus and the obvious way of disposal was to burn the material in the firebox of an engine, hence the straw-burner seen in Fig 94. An extra large firebox was necessary and the grasses were fed in through the aperture into the firehole, more clearly seen in the rear view of the backhead in Fig 95. Another point worthy of note is the transmission, in this case utilising four shafts, viz. the crankshaft, a stud shaft seen just above the rear wheel, the third shaft running across the engine just in front of the throat-plate and the rear axle. The final drive was by the pinion on each end of the third shaft seen inside the rear wheel meshing internally with a toothed ring or annulus attached to the wheel itself. The annulus was shrouded to afford some protection against stones and other débris. Rated at 7 nhp the single cylinder was 8½in x 12in. Several of these engines were exported to Australia, the first being No 2902.

A second design of "Colonial" engine, as this type was called, is illustrated in Figs 96, 97 and 98. Numbered 3053, it was exported to the Argentine and obviously is another straw-burner. As will be noticed from the side views, the boiler was unusually long to provide the extra heating surface necessary for when burning fuels of low calorific value such as bagasse grasses etc. For traversing soft prairie type of land the rear wheels were no less than three feet wide shod with cast iron edge strakes. Although only 3ft 6in diameter, the spoked flywheel had a very heavy rim of 12in face. As in the previous example there were four shafts in the transmission with all four shafts running across the engine in this design.

As the boiler was special also, the main dimensions are worth noting:–

Fig 95 Another view of the Colonial engine.

Tubes	
No.	33
Diameter external	2½in
Length	7ft 8in
Barrel	
Diameter	2ft 9in
Length between tubeplates	7ft 5¾in
Firebox	
Length inside	4ft 2¾in
Width	2ft 2⅛in
Height inside	3ft 1⅝in
Grate area	9·2 sq ft

This large boiler supplied the 12 nhp single cylinder of 10in x 12in at a governed speed of 200 rpm.

As I have stressed earlier a few – perhaps a dozen – four shaft general purpose engines were produced and additional to the specials. A side view of a fine example is to be seen in Fig 99. The juxta position of the four shafts is clearly shown as is another very uncommon feature in a Thetford product, viz. the valve chest, gear and slide valve are on the right-hand side. A single Salter safety valve is placed ahead of the single cylinder, the latter being steam jacketed. A pop-type additional safety valve is mounted on the nearside top of the block. In this engine the flywheel is solid but with the six spokes acting as ribs. An ordinary spoked pattern was used with an additional and detachable wood plate being fitted by the pattern maker on the outside. The 9 nhp single cylinder four shaft engines had a cylinder 9¼in x 12in, the 8 nhp compound cylinders 6¼in and 11in x 12in and the 10T four shaft roller cylinders 5in and 9in x 9in. Note this engine is fitted for oil firing a type of burner very similar to those on the then GER being used.

Fig 96 An engine for the Argentine, No 3053.

Fig 97 Another view of the Argentine engine.

Fig 98 Further view of the engine in Fig 97.

The cultivating or ploughing engines may be said to be specials and were usually only made to order. In Fig 70 we have noted the Universal ploughing engines and now a full view of the winding drum is included in Fig 100 where the drum is fitted on the side of the boiler and equipped with a large gear wheel to its inside rim and driven by a pinion on the end of the crankshaft. The rope upon leaving the drum is led around a large grooved pulley mounted beneath the footplate and then away to the implement at right angles to the longitudinal centre-line of the engine. Usually, the drum accommodated 800 yards of rope. When required, a drum could be fitted either side for working on the single engine or roundabout system. The first made, No 888, had two drums and was exhibited at the Kilburn Show in 1879. Most were made with one drum, however, and worked on the twin engine system, i.e. an engine on each headland.

One important technical point concerns the attachment of the drum to the boiler. Each drum axle forms the end of a strong curved bar, bent in the middle to encircle partially the underside of the barrel, the bar being bolted to a heavy section angle iron ring, one each side, the angles being riveted separately to the shell. A far better job than riveting a plate incorporating a stud shaft, thereby imposing all stresses, and they could be considerable, on a small area of the barrel.

These Universal ploughing engines never seriously rivalled the standard type with the drum horizontal under the boiler, but a fair number of sets were sold and exported to Germany. Some, of 10 nhp, had a single cylinder 10in x 12in and the very large engine rated at 20 nhp had usually single crank compound cylinders 8½in and 14in x 12in. All such engines were based on Percival Everitt's Patent No 3553 sealed on 28th February 1879 and further details will be found under No XVI.

Not all cultivating engines worked on the drum and rope system however and a variety of diggers were patented in this country from time to time. Some were practical, many others were not, but two of the more successful ideas were invented and patented by Thomas Churchward Darby. Of his two types the "Broadside" was made by F. Savage (see No XXXIII) but his later machine was designed to be fitted to any make of traction engine with a few modifications. The Thetford works built several engines for use with the Darby Digger and a fine single crank compound complete with its digger is shown in Fig 101. In this design a series of rotating forks arranged chevron-wise below a frame fitted to the rear of the engine were made to rotate by means of a train of spur gears and bevels, the spur gears being driven of the second motion spur ring. This idea was later used in the Gyrotiller.

Often there are different ways of achieving the same

Fig 99 An uncommon Burrell four-shaft road locomotive.

Fig 100 Universal ploughing engine – a view on the winding drum.

Fig 101 The Darby Digger attached to a Burrell traction engine.

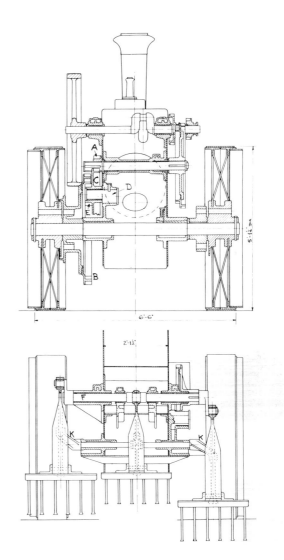

Fig 102 Drawings of a Burrell engine complete with a Proctor Digger.

object and whereas Darby preferred rotating digging forks, his competitor Frank Proctor believed in making his tines approximate to the normal digging action as employed by man. Consequently he obtained Patent No 5956 of 1884 where at the rear of the engine there were placed three sets of forks with six prongs or tines to each – 18 digging elements in all. How they were arranged is clearly shown in the drawings in Fig 102. The final drive pinion A on the left hand end of the countershaft can be moved endwise to the right and out of mesh with the final drive gear B on the rear axle. When moved to its extreme right hand position it becomes meshed with another gear C fixed on a short stub shaft D eccentrically mounted so it can be rotated in or out of gear with A. Combined with C on its left-hand side is a smaller pinion E meshing with an annulur toothed ring cast on the inside of and integral with B. We thus have an extra low gear for when digging at about half the lower road speed and which can be put in or out of gear by rotating the stub shaft D in its eccentric mounting. When digging, motion is trans-mittted from one section of the standard double spur-ring to the digger crankshaft F via the intermediate shaft G carrying the gear wheel H meshing with the final digging shaft gear I. Note that the intermediate shaft G is also eccentrically mounted so that it can be turned out of gear when travelling on the road. These notes should also be read in conjunction with a side view and line diagram included in Fig 103. The digging forks J have their upper ends fixed to the cranks of the digging shaft F which is formed with one internal crank in the centre of its length, and one open overhung crank at each end, the three cranks being arrange at 120°. Each fork contains the six hardened steel tines which work the soil, fitted to the T ends, and each fork proper

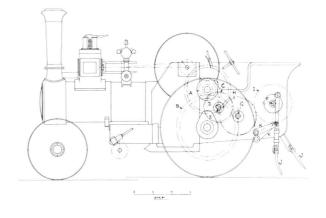

Fig 103 A side view of the Proctor Digger.

is additionally connected to a fixed point at the rear of the engine by the radius links. In this way the tines are given a rearwards scooping motion besides the up and down movement. The Thetford drawing office gained experience of these engines in actual working and between them Frank Proctor and Frederick J. Burrell were granted Patent No 9050 of 12th July 1886, but the details being mainly small modifications hardly concern us here.

A few words in conclusion concerning the works. The sketch map in Fig 104 shows shaded its location and the area covered, 3 acres, 1 rod and 27 perches. The site of St. Nicholas Church was just inside the eastern boundary on the north side of the road. The south side boundary bordered the Little Ouse River and here it was that the small launches and ships were launched. In its heyday the works employed about 400 hands or approximately equal to 10% of the population of Thetford, which at that period was about 4,000.

In the developing period of the firm's progress in the last century, and in the early part of this, a great amount of testing of new designs was carried out in Thetford and its environs, and some of the important incidents have been mentioned. One other test worth recording was between two engines identical save that one had three shafts and the other four, in the transmission.

After exhaustive and prolonged testing up the test hill past Croxton Church, 1 in 17, it was found the three shaft engine could pull on an average a 25% greater load than the four shaft. Which is rather what logic would suggest. The firm pointed out that if one fitted a sufficient number of shafts then at some point there would be no power left at the drawbar for useful work, all the engine's urge being absorbed in overcoming friction.

Fig 105 The great erecting shop at St. Nicholas Works.

Fig 104 Sketch map of St. Nicholas Works, Thetford.

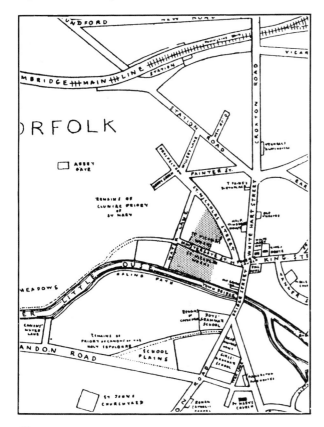

Figs 105, 106 and 107 illustrate views in the works which fortunately have been preserved. Fig 105 shows the magnificent panorama when looking down the big erecting shop towards the river, whilst Fig 106 is a very representative view on the machine shop. Each erector had his own 30 cwt overhead hand-operated travelling crane so no one could loiter and excuse himself by saying he was waiting for a lift! Fig 107 shows the timber swivelling jib cranes used in the foundry. An interesting commentary on the safety at work aspect in those days is to record that a container of carron oil was always available in the foundry so that the slightest burn could be soothed immediately.

Portraits of the family directors prior to World War 1 can be studied in Fig 108 and attached are signatures of Robert Burrell, Charles II, Charles III (C. W. W. Burrell), Frederick John Burrell and Herbert J. Burrell. Such items are not often made available in engineering histories.

Two other items seldom included in such books is a facsimile of the firm's famous letter heading and –much more rare – a share Certificate, and both are to be seen

Fig 106 The machine shop at Thetford.

Fig 107 A timber foundry crane.

in Fig 109. The share Certificate records that Charles II, "the younger" during his father's (Charles I) lifetime held 800 £10 shares in May 1887. An interesting detail is that Frederick J. Burrell, the inventor in the firm, was also Company Secretary at this date.

Most of the buildings forming St. Nicholas Works still stand although the drawing office and large smithy on the north side are razed. The pattern and carpenter's shop are still used by a local firm for wood-working, the remaining buildings of the north side are used for the feather sorting industry. On the south side the canning of foods was carried out for many years in what were the erecting, boiler and machine shops but these have since been razed and the site downgraded to a supermarket! Robert Burrell's house, the garden of which was part of

Mr CHARLES BURRELL

Mr CHARLES BURRELL JUNR.

Mr ROBERT G. BURRELL

Mr FREDK J. BURRELL.

Charles Burrell

C. W. W. Burrell.
Directors

H. J. Burrell Secretary

Robt G. Burrell

Fredk J Burrell

Fig 108 Portraits of some of the Burrell family and signatures.

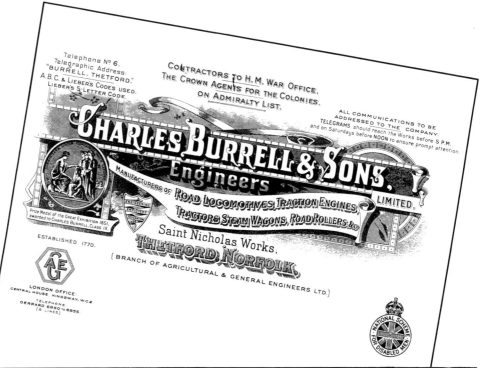

Fig 109 A Burrell letter heading and a Share Certificate.

the graveyard of St. Nicholas Church, has been converted into a restaurant.

The Thetford drawing office over the years must have devoted some time to the design of nameplates suitable for the various types of engines and Fig 110 illustrates seven of the eight different designs used over a period of about half a century, each with its dimensions as follow:

a)– Oval No 857. Ploughing engine of 1879. 11⅝in x 7¼in. Brass.

b)– Partly oval No 942. Portable of 1881. 12in x 5¼in. Bronze.

c)– Oval No 980. Traction of 1881. 11½in x 7½in. Cast iron.

d)– Rectangular No 1087. Traction of 1884. 9¾in x 8⅝in. Cast iron.

e)– Rectangular No 3676. Traction of 1915. 7⅝in x 6½in. Brass.

f)– Rectangular of Patent Compound Engine. 7⅝in x 5⅝in. Brass.

g)– Oval No 3953. Wagon of 1924. 11⅝in x 7⅜in. Brass.

h)– Circular. Smokebox door centre. 7in diameter. Cast iron.

i)– Rectangular as (e) but with no number. 7⅝in x 6½in. Brass.

c

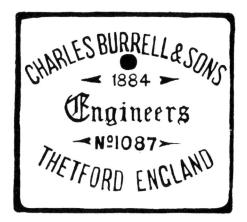

d

a

b

Fig 110 A pride of Burrell nameplates.

e

f

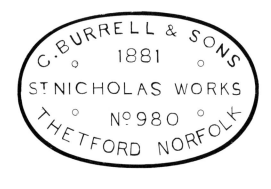

g

h

i

M I Mech E, a director of the Wellworthy Piston Ring Company and an old Burrell apprentice, on 12th July 1958. It measures 24in x 22in x 2½in and is a beautiful example of casting by the *cire perdu* method.

As a fitting and appropriate conclusion to this great Norfolk firm I include a picture in Fig 112 of the last Burrell engine made at Leiston Works after the transfer, in 1932. It bears the work's number 4094 and happily is still existing in working order.

Fig 111 The Burrell Memorial.

Fig 112 The last Burrell traction engine, No 4094.

One variant not illustrated and rather uncommon was similar to (i) but with the word "Engineers" in Old English black letter. Apparently very few of these plates were fitted. All the above are from the author's collection.

To remind the visitor to this ancient capital of East Anglia that this area was once a hive of production and industry, the Burrell Memorial was erected on the south external wall of the original general offices on the north side of Minstergate Street. It takes the form seen in Fig 111 of a three-dimension casting in bronze of the first 1856 Burrell-Boydell engine with a suitable inscription below. Subscribed for by public subscription it was unveiled by the late John Howlett OBE,

VII

EDGAR C. BURRELL & SONS LTD.,
Southtown, GREAT YARMOUTH.

A firm established in 1884 by William Burrell, having no connection with No VI and which still exists, having been carried on latterly by his sons.

The steam engine side was commenced by William Burrell to meet the demand for marine engines arising from the application of steam power in the fishing industry and the increasing number of small coasters.

For the smaller vessels a fine design of compound surface condensing engine was produced and one such is illustrated in Fig 113 having cylinders 12in and 26in x 18in. They were very compact, their overall dimensions being only 8ft 6in long x 9ft 0in high x 6ft 8in wide, thus not occupying very much space in a fishing vessel where space was at a premium. Their rating was 240 ihp, each cylinder was a separate casting and both cylinders were secured to the bedplate by turned polished steel columns in front and by cast iron standards at the back. The air, feed, circulating and bilge pumps were separate units mounted on the bedplate at the rear of the engine and worked from a pump lever by the low pressure crosshead direct. Both pistons were of close-grained cast iron with Lockwood & Carlisle rings and springs with loose junk rings, and there was a piston valve to the high pressure and a D slide valve to the low pressure. As will be seen from

Fig 113 A compound surface condensing marine engine by E. C. Burrell of Yarmouth.

Fig 114 300 hp triple expansion engine by Edgar C. Burrell.

Fig 113 they were very good looking engines. Two smaller sizes could be made to order where the strokes were 16in and 14in.

For larger powers a straight triple was available having cylinders 10in and 17in and 28in x 18in producing 300 ihp with steam at 210 psi. One is to be seen in Fig 114 and the remaining specification was

Fig 115 A fine E. C. Burrell marine type engine for
a sawmill.

similar to that for the compound save that the low
pressure slide valve is of the Andrews & Cameron
balanced type instead of the ordinary flat design. In this
engine the overall dimensions were 9ft 9in long x
8ft 3in high x 6ft 9in wide.

With a few minor modifications these engines could
be adapted for land use and a very fine example was
made in 1923 and installed in Messrs. Wenns Timber
Sawmills locally in Yarmouth. A view of it is included in
Fig 115. Slightly under 300 ihp it had cylinders 10in
and 16½in and 26½in x 18in and bore the work's
number 60. It was a really fine example of marine
engineering but regretfully it has now been scrapped.

✧ VIII ✧
F. W. CARVER,
GREAT YARMOUTH. Southtown Dock,

Francis William Carver first started in Yarmouth when
he came to superintend the erection of two drifter
engines built by Davis & Co. in London. Subsequently
in 1900 he started on his own to manufacture engines in
a small shop rented from Messrs. Fellows on their
property in Southtown Road. Finally closing down in
1930, the works were then taken over by the
landlords.

Both compound and triple expansion engines were
made, the first being a compound which was installed in

a steamer called the *Claudian* followed by one or two
others, one being installed in the steam drifter *Triumph*
and having cylinders 11in and 22in x 15in. Later, a
piston valve was fitted to the high pressure cylinder, the
slide valve being retained for the low pressure. Solid
expansion links were used containing a groove in the
inside of which worked the die-block. The next smaller
size had cylinders 10in and 20in x 14in. A third and
smallest in the range is illustrated in Fig 116 where the
cylinders were 6½in and 13in x 10in, and the
photograph shows clearly all the main features of a very
neat design of a typical small English marine engine.
This engine, incidentally, was built in 1909 and for
many years powered an ex-Naval pinnace named
Terrible which plied for many years on the River Yare.
Upon this vessel being scrapped the engine was lifted
out complete and set down on the marshes night unto
Whitlingham railway station and in the parish of
Thorpe St. Andrew. It was photographed in 1955 but
sadly it is not now to be found!

The triples came towards the end of the period of
production and embodied the same details as did the
compound engines, the first being used in a large drifter
called the *Selene Salmon*, a Yarmouth built boat. The
cylinders were 9in and 14in and 25in x 18in. All had
independent air pumps and condensers and were fitted
with a piston valve to the high pressure cylinder.

Fig 116 F. W. Carver's compact compound surface
condensing engine.

A few small launch engines were produced to order and in design and configuration they resembled closely their larger brethren. They had cylinders 6in and 12in x 10in.

IX

JOHN COLLINGS,
The Hall Works, BACTON.

John Maris Bejamin Collings, born in 1882, was the only son of John Collings and Margaret his wife, the only daughter of Benjamin and Margaret Stannard. Benjamin Stannard was one of a family of six and his elder sister Elizabeth married Robert Holmes whose great aunt Ann Holmes was grandmother to Anna Sewell, 1820–1878, the authoress of that immortal classic *Black Beauty*. Further back on his mother's side there were connections through the Buxtons to the Parrs, Catherine Parr becoming the ultimate wife Henry VIII. The Parrs were wealthy watchmakers and jewellers of London and John Collings used and showed with pride a large "turnip" type of watch made by one of the Parr family. His mother's great grandfather, Benjamin Stannard, died 1815, had married Susannah Parr.

The family of Collings came from versatile stock and in several Norwich city churches there are lapidary slabs to the Collings family dated 1639, 1690, 1700, 1727 and 1729. At Walcot is a slab to John Collings, STP, born 1623 and died 1690. In Brancaster church there is a brass to Magister William Collyng, rector of Brancaster in 1457 who died in 1480.

It was from his father's side that John inherited his mechanical bent for John senior was a threshing contractor, land owner and merchant of Bacton. Therefore John junior naturally became well versed in the mechanics and maintenance of agricultural machinery of the 1870s. His father had at that time taken up residence in Bacton Hall.

In the precincts of the Hall he built up little by little his own small works, added one of the largest wheel-turning lathes in Norfolk, laid down a small ferrous and non-ferrous foundry and later drove the whole lot electrically. His first power unit was a small overtype steam engine by Savage of Lynn belted to the line shafting. Later, he substituted a Fairbanks-Morse oil engine belted to a two-pole Edmundson dynamo with gauze brushes – a sight to delight the eye of the connoisseur!

From time to time he retired to his small outbuilding between the Hall and the little works which served him as pay, general and drawing office and being a self-taught draughtsman, committed to paper his divers brainwaves. A number got beyond the drawing board and as far as HM Patent Office. Altogether ten patents were applied for of which seven were eventually sealed. The complete list is as follows:–

No 9750 of 26th April 1907. For sowing and harrowing.

No 12831 of 1907. For tractors.

No 26516 of 19th November 1912. For a petrol pourer and strainer.

No 29729 of 24th December 1912. For multiple ploughs.

No 1350 of 17th January 1913. For closing tyre punctures.

No 17013 of 17th July 1914. For locomotives.

No 105671 fo 1916. For ploughs.

No 146592 of 1919. For ploughs.

No 28909 of 13th December 1919. For scissors and sharpener.

No 169296 of 1920. For ploughs.

Those not sealed were Nos 1350, 26516 and 28909. Even so, seven out of ten constitutes a very good score.

His self-lift plough and cultivator was suitable for direct traction and the cultivator could be fitted with nine or eleven tines. The ploughs could accommodate from two to seven shares and like the cultivator were equipped with Collings' auto-lifting gear whereby the power of the tractor is made to lift the implement out of work.

To ease the task of the agriculturist still further, the maker's plough could be used with, and attached to it, a harrow, roller and seed drill.

A sympathetic background, this was to foster John Collings' liking for the steam engine and as the list of patents show No 17013 of 17th July 1914 was devoted to a four cylinder locomotive wherein the cylinders were arranged in two pairs in tandem, each pair to have a high and low pressure cylinder viz. each pair was a tandem compound. In addition, all cylinders were to be jacketed by extending the bottom of the smokebox downwards and around them so that the hot gases from the tubes diminished radiation of heat from, and condensation of steam in, the cylinders.

As he once remarked to me, the self-moving engine, either road or rail, attracted him more than other types so it is not surprising the three engines he made were all road engines. His first was a small light steam motor tractor, at this time now legal by the Heavy Motor Car Orders of 1903, which was completed in February 1905.

Fig 117 John Collings' No 1 small chain road engine.

Fig 118 Front offside view of Collings' No 1 engine.

Fig 119 View on the backhead of No 1.

One view of it is to be seen in Fig 117. It had duplex cylinders 3½in x 6in mounted over the firebox, with slide valves on the outside, the valves operated by Stephenson's link motion. Several unusual features are to be found in its construction : for example, the boiler was mounted on a form of independent chassis to relieve it of an amount of stress during work and the rear axle was mounted on springs. This chassis was built from 1in x 3in flat bar on edge and extended forward to carry the front axle, the smokebox being attached just behind it. In this way the smokebox was relieved of all stresses due to the front axle. The rear axle turned in bearings free to rise and fall in guides, each being connected to a semi-elliptic spring below, the springs being just visible in Fig 117. Two speeds were incorporated in the transmission, comprising a twin spur-ring rotating on a stud shaft beneath the crankshaft with the two necessary pinions on the end of the last named shaft. The spur-ring seen in Fig 117 in turn drove the third shaft; on the offside end of it seen in Fig 118 is the small sprocket forming the final drive to the rear axle, in fact the very slack chain is still around the sprocket in the photograph. Another interesting detail is that a second chain could be used around the large chain wheel on the third shaft in Fig 119 and a sprocket just inside the flywheel, when with the gears in neutral the engine became a three shaft machine with the spur-ring merely an idler. The engine could be managed easily by one man as the designer intended, the controls all being within easy reach of the driver as will be apparent from Fig 119. With the exception of the boiler and cylinder castings, which were from G. S. Soame (see No. XXXV), all the rest of this little engine was made in the works in the Hall grounds.

Five years later, in 1910, the second Bacton-built engine appeared, again designed to be classed as a steam motor tractor and in fact it weighed unladen 4 ton 12 cwt. A view of it looking on the offside is depicted in Fig 120. In this case John Collings used tandem

compound cylinders 5in and 8in x 8in using steam at 250 psi and a sectional drawing of the block is shown in Fig 121. All these drawings of the Collings engines were prepared by the writer from the maker's original

Fig 120 Collings' No 2 tandem compound, the offside prospect.

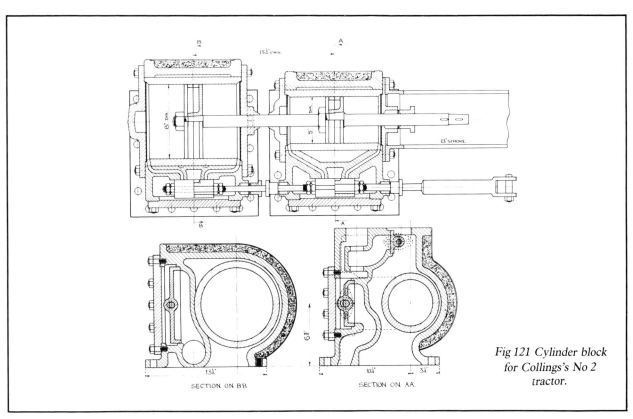

SECTION ON BB

SECTION ON AA.

Fig 121 Cylinder block for Collings's No 2 tractor.

drawings and sketches given to him not long before Collings' death. Owing to the ravages of time, the originals were too faded and torn to be suitable for reproduction. Note the great simplicity of the motion work for the two cylinders, and the very light but aesthetically pleasing canopy. Incidentally, this engine and No 3 were both rated at 4 nhp.

The rear springing seen in Fig 122 is quite simple, utilising a semi-elliptical multi-leaf spring each side which absorbed road shocks considerably. Up and down movement of the rear axle was allowed for in the final drive by making the teeth of both pinion and gear straight sided for part of their height. This engine is owned and used by the author who can testify to the excellence of the springing.

In Fig 123 we have a nearside view of Collings' No 2 taken when in use on a public road. The width over the rear wheels is 6ft 11in and over the front 3ft 7in. The maker used this engine a great deal for direct ploughing and other agricultural jobs and a picture of it hauling a batch of sail binders is included in Fig 124. Its registration number was originally AH 047 but is now AH 47. This is because Norfolk may have been the only county which used in the early days the same registration letters for motorcycles, cars and other vehicles but at the same time using three sets of

Fig 122 John Collings' design of rear springing.

numbers. Thus at one time, as the erstwhile owner of a motorcycle AH 1 tells me, it was possible to see a car also bearing AH 1 in the same street in Norwich! The differentiation for other vehicles was made by prefixing a nought to the figures so that the first would be AH 01, which accounts for why the Collings engines bore the numbers AH 047 and AH 0272. With the Road Traffic

Fig 123 Nearside view of No 2 on the road.

Fig 124 No 2 drawing sail binders.

Act all three series were brought together with a common AH prefix.

In this period as is the case today, every vehicle had to have a Registration Certificate and as many readers may never have seen one, that for Collings No 3 is reproduced in Fig 125. Note an official error – the weight on the front axle = 1 ton 9 hundredweights, and on the rear 3 tons. But the total is stated as 4 tons 19 hundredweights, or half a ton too much! Those familiar with the Stranger's Hall, Norwich may be interested to know that the then Registrar, H.C. Bolingbroke whose signature appears on the

Fig 125 Registration Certificate for Collings' No 3 engine.

Certificate in Fig 125, was the brother of L. Bolingbroke Esq. who gave to the city this gem of a mediaeval house for all time.

Coming now to Collings' last engine No 3. This was also a tandem compound with cylinders 5in and 8in x 8in but fitted with piston valves instead of slide valves and the details of this block can be studied in Fig 126. This block was quite different to that used on No 2 because this had the cylinders linered into one outer casting whereas No 2 had separate cylinders each mounted on a steel base plate riveted to the boiler shell. Also piston valves were fitted being 3⅜in and 4in diameter for the HP and LP respectively and the outer casting was fitted direct on to the boiler shell.

In Fig 127 we have an offside view of No 3 showing the differences in the cylinder block, the square top to

COUNTY OF NORFOLK.
FORM A.
COPY OF REGISTER OF HEAVY MOTOR CARS.

Chas. Knight & Co., Ltd., Tooley Street, S.E.—(16029-1913)

Index Mark and Number on Identification Plates. 1.	Full Name of Owner and Postal Address of his usual Residence. 2.	Description or Type of Car. 3.	Type and Colour of Body of Car. 4.	Weight unladen. 5.	Axle-weight of each Axle. 6.	Diameter of Wheels. 7.	Width and Material of Tyres. 8.	Maximum Speed Permissible. 9.	Whether intended for			Date of Registration. 11.	If Cancelled, date of Cancellation. 12.
									(a) Private use.	(b) Use for Trade Purposes.	(c) Use as a Public Conveyance.		
A.H. 0272	John Maris Collings Baston Nth Walsham Nfk	4 HP Collings	Tractor	4 Tons 19 cwts	Front 1 Ton 9 cwts Hind 3 Tons	Front 3ft 4in Hind 5ft 6in	Front 7 inches Hind 12 inches Iron tyres	5 miles per hour		Trade		1915 Nov 29	
										by Bolingbroke Registrar.			

81

the smokebox to accommodate a superheater and belly tanks. Completed in 1915 No 3 was then used in place of No 2 to do all the power work required on the agricultural estate connected with Bacton Hall.

John Collings bought his boilers out, one from Messrs. Farrers of Newark and the other from Alfred Dodman of Lynn. Both had a heating surface of 84 square feet.

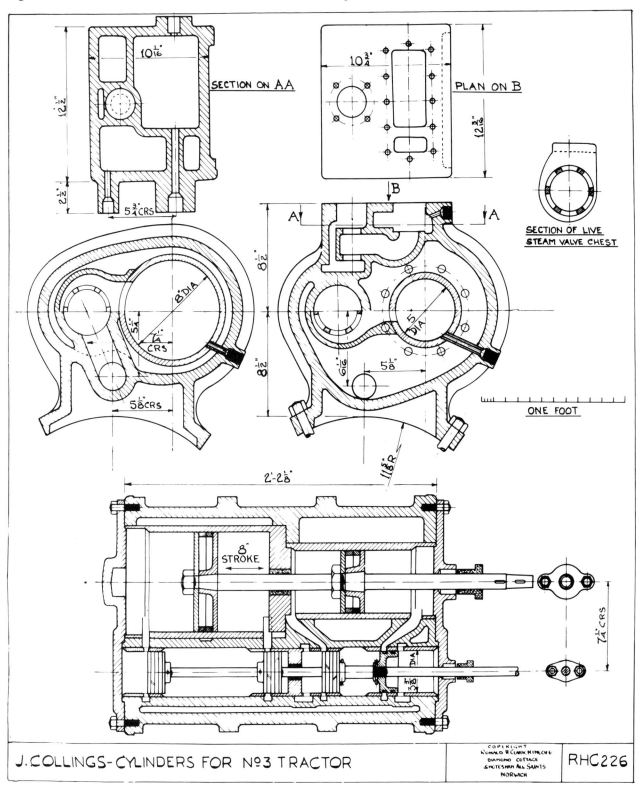

J. COLLINGS - CYLINDERS FOR Nº 3 TRACTOR

COPYRIGHT
RONALD H CLARK M.I.MECH.E
DIAMOND COTTAGE
SHOTESHAM ALL SAINTS
NORWICH

RHC226

Fig 126 The tandem compound cylinder block for Collings' No 3.

Fig 127 Rare offside view of the Bacton No 3 tractor.

John Collings greatly admired two leading steam designers, Samuel Vauclain of the Baldwin Works in America and F. G. Smith, then locomotive engineer on the Highland Railway. Several hints he derived from Vauclain's designs he embodied in No 2 and he told me when designing No 3 he had in mind the 10in diameter long travel piston valves Smith had used in his famous Rivers class 4-6-0 express engines for the Highland Railway in 1915 where the cylinders were 21in x 28in. It will be seen therefore that Collings' proportion of valve bore to cylinder bore compares very favourably with Smith's design. It was an excellent example of a country engineer keeping abreast of current developments by a study of the contemporary technical press.

During September 1918 a ploughing test was carried out on his estate at Bacton using one of his patent cultivators. In reporting this rather remarkable performance the *Eastern Daily Press* concluded by stating "*All the machinery Mr. Collings builds is of interchangeable parts, made entirely under the inventor's supervision, and he takes pride in the fact, that apart from his smith, all his men are discharged soldiers, or rejected from the army on medical grounds, and entirely trained in their present work by Mr. Collings*".

During the Second World War shortage of solid fuel caused him to cease using steam for direct traction and as a result No 3, which was left in the open because of the difficulty in erecting new buildings, became derelict and the last view taken of it is to be seen in Fig 128. No 2, however, he was able to store under cover.

Fig 128 No 3 derelict.

During the war he had perforce to work his agricultural business at times single handed, causing him to neglect the Hall (the gardens were at one time a veritable show place) and after his mother's death (he was a bachelor), other and domestic chores. He also neglected his own creature comforts and was found dead in his own home on 23rd January 1950, aged 68 years. He was laid to rest beside his mother at Bacton, close to the site of his small works where he had spent so much of his life.

I knew John Collings for a number of years. He was a well-built man with dark penetrating eyes, a deep soft voice and plenty of energy for the job in hand. During the winter in 1947 when by snow most North Norfolk roads were impassable, he made himself a pair of snow shoes on which to travel to North Walsham for a train to Norwich. Once I remember how the manageress raised her eyebrows when, in a well-known teashop, he parked his snow shoes upright alongside the coat stand!

To conclude, Fig 129 shows a corner of the works rather neglected in later years. On the left can be seen part of the big faceplate of the wheel-turning lathe and to the right is the multiple spindle drill. For good measure we have in Fig 130 a copy of John Collings' letter heading and lower down his signature, together with two name-plates, now on the author's No 2 Collings engine.

To finish No 3 the maker, owing to war-time difficulties in getting certain parts, cannibalised some items off No 2. Later, when No 3 was being dismantled, all necessary parts were replaced on No 2 to make it "as made".

Fig 129 A corner of John Collings' small workshop.

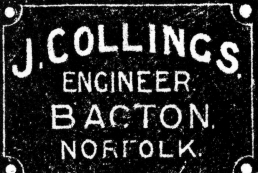

Fig 130 Collings' letter heading and nameplates.

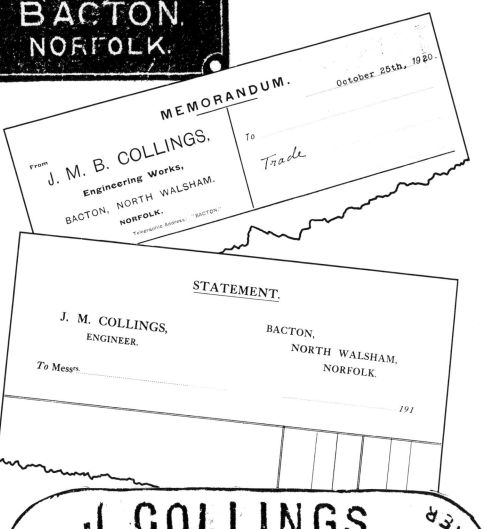

X

THE COOPER STEAM DIGGER CO. LTD., Wisbech Road Steel Works, KING'S LYNN.

Thomas Cooper was originally managing director of the Farmer's Foundry Co. (No. XVI) and after evolving his Patent Steam Digger, left the Ryburgh concern and started an entirely new works on the Wisbech Road a little prior to 1890, on purpose to produce this digger. Another invention of his was his split roller bearing and later these took the place of the digging machinery, the firm then becoming the Cooper Roller Bearings Co. Ltd. as it still exists.

The principles of Cooper's arrangement should be clarified by the old photograph in Fig 131 where two rows of forks are used, each row being two feet apart and formed of four groups of equidistant prongs, each group of prongs forming a digging fork. Thus there are 40 prongs in all. Those in the front row are chisel shaped, flat and sharp, and enter the ground very easily, whilst those in the second row are curved to break up the soil turned by the first row. From a study of Fig 131 it will be seen the forks move with a circular motion in a vertical plane, the point of each describing a trochoid. The main cross-shaft is driven by the engine, the cranks giving the motion to the frames and their prongs. This motion imitates very closely the movements of a spade when used by hand and is very pretty to watch, as the cranks ensure that the forks on each bar enter the ground together, the others following in natural sequence. A travelling shoe in contact with the ground on each side of the frame following all irregularities in the terrain keeps the digging depth constant. An hydraulic cylinder worked off the engine pump is provided to raise or lower the whole digging frame, as required. When travelling on the road and used as a traction engine, the gear is raised by the cylinder and locked in the "up" position. Of course the forks are driven into the ground by their resistance against the engine.

In 1900 a digger of this design was tested at the RAS Show at Kexby near York on 14 and 15th June by the late Prof. W. E. Dalby. Following are the brief details:-

Cylinders	6½in and 11½in x 12in
Working pressure psi	150
ihp digging lightly	32.04 @ 217 rpm
Average speed	24.7 yards per minute
Area dug per minute	78.5 sq yards
ihp digging heavily	40.09 @ 202 rpm
Average speed	23.0 yards per minute
Area dug per minute	73.2 sq yards

Fig 131 Thomas Cooper's first design of steam digger.

The plot was 1.25 acres in area requiring 150 minutes, which is the equivalent of half an acre per hour or roughly four acres per day.

Indicator diagrams taken during the test are included in Fig 132 which show the good steam distribution, both expansion lines cutting each other at half stroke. Had slightly stronger springs been used I think the lines would have been smoother.

It will be seen these early Cooper diggers followed almost normal traction engine practice in the rest of their design, having two road speeds of two and three and a half mph. Rear wheels were 5ft 9in diameter x 26in wide for digging or 20in wide when fitted to an engine without digging gear. Front wheels were 3ft 6in diameter x 12in wide and like the Collings engines (see No IX) had a narrower track than the rear. Total weight in digging order was 11 tons 18½ hundredweights, of which 8 tons 15 hundredweights was on the rear wheels. Overall price was £750 as the digging gear, unlike that of the Darby, was not sold separately.

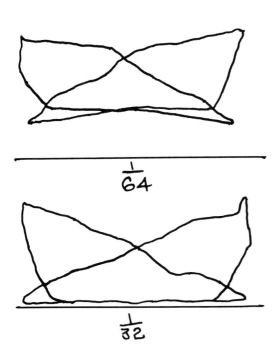

Fig 132 Indicator diagrams from the Cooper Digger on test.

Design seldom stands still and in Fig 133 is shown an example of Cooper's second type where the traction engine layout is retained but the digging gear has been re-designed to be driven by a heavy duty roller chain which, with some of the operating mechanism to the forks, is enclosed. The engine in this illustration was being erected in Egypt. Note the accessible position of the pump supplying the hydraulic lifting cylinder.

Other Cooper diggers were exported to Egypt and

one at work there is shown in Fig 134. This illustrates very clearly the pump and ends of the piston rods, crossheads and so on all enclosed. It is said that about two dozens of such machines were sent to Egypt in the period up to World War 1.

Fig 133 The roller chain drive on Cooper's digger.

Fig 134 Another Cooper Digger working in Egypt.

To relieve the boiler of as much stress as possible, Cooper produced another version where the engine itself, motion and digging gear, were all compactly-mounted at the rear of the engine, as may be examined in Fig 135. Note that each fork now possesses six prongs with the hydraulic cylinder central in the back in this case.

The machine in Fig 135 should be studied in conjunction with a very similar engine in Fig 136, showing the nearside and especially the worm and geared steering. Thus all sagging chains and lost motion are eliminated. Why more makers did not adopt such positive steering always mystifies me.

Fig 135 Cooper's digging gear arranged at the rear.

Fig 136 Nearside view showing the steering, 1905 heavy type engine.

To cut down weight as far as possible Cooper created in 1903 another design using only three wheels, as will be seen from the illustration in Fig 137. Three-wheeled engines were not new as we have seen but here is a later and improved version. For example, the boiler was of the quick steaming return tube type and had the totally enclosed oil-bath lubricated engine mounted on top. Cooper claimed the great advantage was the driver

being seated right forward could see better where he was going and therefore could steer and negotiate the unit much easier.

In Fig 138 is a view on the digging mechanism at the rear, illustrating the robustness of the triangular frames and the three prongs now forming each fork. The rear wheels are now castings and unlike ordinary traction engines have the cast-in strakes square across the treads. These engines were, of course, also very suitable for belt driving when the belt would be taken rearwards off the flywheel, the Pickering governors taking care of the speed.

Known in the works as their No 5, these machines would dig four to six acres per day requiring only one to two hundredweights of best coal per acre. On the road they could do 6 mph. If the customer desired, single or double winding drums could be fitted in place of the digging gear as shown in Fig 139. A single drum required 400 yards of rope but with double drums 300 was needed for one drum and 600 for the other. Both drums had automatic band brakes and guide pulleys were fitted under the boiler. Other main details were:−

Cylinders	4¾in and 8in x 9in
Tubes	50 x 1⅝in O/D
Working pressure	180 psi
Test pressure	300 psi
Heating surface	85 sq feet + feed water heater
EHP	25 @ 250/300 rpm
Width overall	5ft 10in
Tank capacity	120 gallon
Bunker capacity	6 cwt

Fig 137 Cooper's three wheeled engine.

Fig 138 The rear digging gear on the three wheeled-engine.

Fig 139 View on the winding drum end of a Cooper engine.

As will be noticed, the four forks had three renewable prongs and would dig a spit 5ft 10in wide but for light soils an extension could be fitted enabling a spit 6ft 10in wide to be dug. There were change gears incorporated to give 4, 5 or 6 inches travel for each stroke of the forks. When digging at the usual rate of 150/200 rpm an average depth dug was nine inches. With the present day accent on interchangeability it is interesting to note that Cooper made all spare parts interchangeable.

Fortunately I am able to have reproduced in Fig 140 what some may deem an interesting, almost social document, showing the firm's notepaper heading and Cooper's signature. As reproduced it may be slightly difficult to read and therefore I include a transcript as follows:–

"*Godfrey Banham has been employed by me as apprentice and workman for seven years, and I have great pleasure in bearing testimony to the very satisfactory manner he conducted himself throughout. He has had a varied experience and is a capable mechanic – and is competent to take charge of engines and machinery. He is both industrious and attentive to duty and having often been employed by me in business matters of a confidential nature and I am able to say that he is thoroughly trustworthy and honest. Feeling sure that he will prove his worth in whatever capacity he may be employed I have the greatest pleasure in giving him my heartiest recommendation, added to my best wishes for his success*".

THOMAS COOPER

Certainly this document proves that at times amicable relationships do exist between employer and employee.

Fig 140 A facsimile letter from Thomas Cooper.

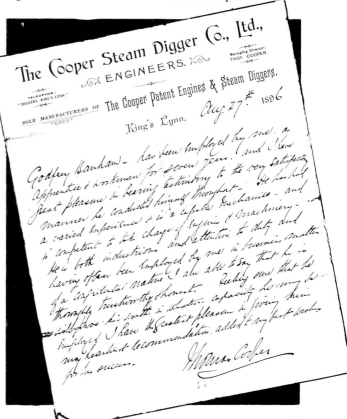

XI

CRABTREE (1931) LTD.,
Southtown Ironworks, GREAT YARMOUTH.

Established by William F. Crabtree in 1854 near Southtown railway station, the firm eventually acquired the site formerly occupied by Robert Barnes (see No III) when they moved to their present works in 1900. Later, they became Crabtree & Sons Ltd and finally reconstructed as shown by the title above. Shortly after World War 2 they were taken over by F. T. Everard & Sons Ltd, and then early in 1970 Richards (Shipbuilders) Ltd, of Lowestoft acquired them and simultaneously Messrs. Fellows Shipyard. For economic reasons Messrs. Richards closed down the Crabtree works and shops at the end of March 1970.

Crabtree's speciality, as may be assumed, was making marine engines, both compound and triple expansion types. A typical early design of compound is shown in Fig 141 which, although only small, clearly illustrates the main details. Note the three holding-down bolts each side in the bedplate. They ranged from cylinders 6in and 12in x 8in to very large engines with cylinders 20in and 43in x 30in. Two of the small compounds were fitted in the small twin screw passenger steamer *Norwich Belle*, at one time well known on the Norfolk rivers.

Fig 142 Second type of Crabtree's compound surface condensing engine.

Fig 143 Crabtree's famous straight triple condensing marine engine.

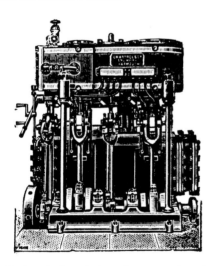

Fig 141 Crabtree's first design of compound marine engine.

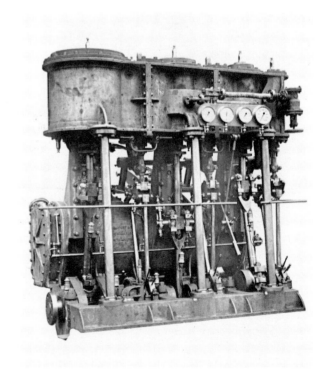

Some modifications as experience suggested were incorporated in later examples and one of these is illustrated in Fig 142. Note the different design of bedplate and the absence of a flywheel.

Their straight triple was a very handsome machine indeed as may be seen from Fig 143 and used in the larger ocean-going Icelandic design of trawlers. Of 700 ihp the cylinders were 17in, 27in and 43in x 27in and some were fitted in tugs for the Canadian Pacific

Railway. For the ordinary drifter and trawler a smaller triple was produced having cylinders 9in, 14½in and 23in x 16in. During World War 1 a number were supplied to the British Admiralty having cylinders 11¾in, 19½in and 32in x 22in for use in vessels designed specifically for mine sweeping.

The main points in the specification of all these fine engines comprise the condenser being part of the main engine, auxiliary steam valve for the low pressure cylinder operated from the starting platform, Cameron corrugated rings to pistons, double bar pattern expansion links, and reversing gear either hand or steam-operated, the thrust bearing designed on the "horseshoe" principle being part of the bedplate with the collars working on white metal faces of large surface and adjustable in fore and aft direction. It is not now certain if any Crabtree engines still exist.

XII

DANIEL CROWE,
Victoria Steam Works, GAYWOOD.

Daniel Crowe commenced as a wheelwright and blacksmith in about 1860 and had a small shop close to the Lynn-Hunstanton railway crossing in Gaywood. In deference to the fame of the then reigning monarch in the middle of the last century he called his premises Victoria Steam Works.

Two very interesting and original steam engines were made in his works, the first being a self-moving threshing machine exhibited at the RAS at Bury St. Edmunds in July 1867. Two views of this unusual machine are shown in Fig 144. It will be noted that the implement was like an ordinary threshing machine of this period save that it was naturally a little longer and had a tall hinged chimney at one end. The engine, at the same end, was of the crank-overhead type with a single cylinder taking steam from a dry-back type of boiler with return tubes, so that the chimney was placed at the same end as the firebox and above it. The engine drove all the motions in the machine by belts, the exception being the fan which was driven by friction wheels. When moving on the road these motions were disconnected and rotation given to the rear road driving wheels by pinions meshing with an internal toothed annulus on each road wheel. These pinions were friction driven by another friction wheel on the crankshaft, in effect a three shaft transmission.

A year later, in July 1868, Crowe had formed his business into the Gaywood Agricultural Co. which was really a concern floated to promote his ideas and they (in July 1868) again exhibited this combined machine at

Fig 144 Daniel Crowe's combined road engine and threshing machine.

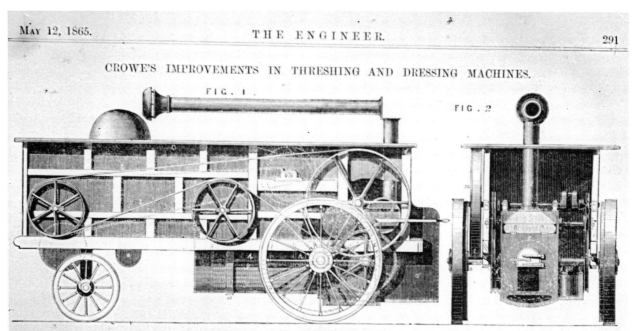

the Leicester Show. It weighed 7 tons 1 hundredweight and on test at the show threshed forty-four stones of inferior wheat (not attempted by other exhibitors) in nine minutes. Crowe stated that when travelling from Towcester to Bury St. Edmunds under its own steam, eighty four miles, the fuel consumption was of 16 lbs of coal per mile.

The second Crowe engine was a traction engine mounted on two rear driving wheels with a single wide steering roller in front, a three-wheel vehicle. Fortunately I am able to illustrate this very unusual and interesting road engine in Fig 145. It will be seen that steerage was in front operated by the ship's wheel mechanism of the period and power was developed in a large single cylinder, the dimensions unfortunately not now known. An extensive footplate extended breast high round both sides of the boiler and the intrepid were restrained from accidents by the wrought iron railings to match. Crowe used it for many years on local haulage work and it is stated that it carted the bricks during the building of Lynn Grammar School. Later it spent some years in Ely and Thetford before being broken up. It was probably built c1875.

Daniel Crowe had an excellent reputation locally as a trustworthy man and during the final stages of construction of the Lynn & Fakenham Railway in 1877/8, the railway company ordered several 4-4-0 tank locomotives from Hudswell, Clarke & Rogers of Leeds.

Fig 145 The unusual three-wheeled engine by Daniel Crowe.

When completed, two, named *Hillington* and *Fakenham*, the makers were instructed to consign to Daniel Crowe, "Gaywood Sidings". His job was to off-load, steam them and make sure all was in order before entering service on the new railway finally opened to Great Massingham on 16th August 1879. It is interesting to note Crowe's Victoria Steam Works had its own sidings and access to what was then the GER Lynn to Hunstanton branch, now all destroyed.

CUBITT & SON,
Market Place, NORTH WALSHAM.

George Cubitt was classified as an Ironmonger, Brazier & Founder in 1845 and as an Engineer, Ironfounder etc. with premises in the Market Place in 1864. By 1875 the business was known as Cubitt & Son and continued as such until 1883, after which one finds no mention of them but apparently F. Randell, Agricultural Engineer, acquired the site after 1883. A certain George Cubitt, however, had a coffee house in the Market Place in 1888.

In 1878 it was George Cubitt who exhibited a small steam engine at the North Walsham Show described as "made by the exhibitor", but precise details are lacking. It appears to have been a horizontal engine with a single cylinder and must have been representative of this period. It was listed at £70 but how many were made is not known.

XIV

ALFRED DODMAN & CO. LTD.,
Highgate Works, KING'S LYNN.

Alfred Dodman was born in Tichwell in 1832, the first child of Martin and Elizabeth Dodman. Strangely, there is no baptismal record in Tichwell's registers although there are for the later children, commencing in 1836. Martin Dodman was a corn and coal merchant in Thornham and a farmer in Tichwell. In the early 1870s he owned 342 acres, obviously a man of some standing and substance.

When of age Alfred was apprenticed to Clayton & Shuttleworth Ltd. of Lincoln and after serving his time started in Lynn. Assuming he left school at fourteen and served his time in five years, he would have been only nineteen when he commenced a kind of "one man and a boy" establishment c1851 in Austin Street.

Robert Southgate Baker (see No II) had had small premises in the same street in 1845, but by 1854 he had moved to a larger site in Blackfriar's Road and probably a little later Dodman occupied Baker's first small works.

In an Agreement dated 8th December 1854 between Charles Willett of King's Lynn, ironmonger; and Alfred Dodman of Tichwell, engineer; witnessed by Martin Dodman, it was arranged for Alfred Dodman to lease for seven years "*all those workshops, warehouses, and shops with the Counting-house, yards and appurtenances thereto belonging to and now occupied by the said Charles Willett situate in Baker's Lane in King's Lynn – abutting a dwelling house, belonging to the said Charles Willett and in the possession of Chittleburgh in one part and in the said lane in the other part towards the North on premises of Edward Everard & Sons towards the South and East*". It was dated 25th March 1855 for a yearly rent of £70. Dodman agreed to buy "*The two Steam Engines with all machinery, gearing, shafting and forges, fixtures, fittings, stock of materials, models, tools and gas fittings and all other articles – except the Braziers, Tinmans and Gunsmiths tools*").

Willett agreed not to manufacture or repair any steam machinery whatsoever during the period of the lease, and Dodman was given the option of buying the premises for the sum of £1,250.

Dodman was now well established because in the *Lynn News Advertiser* for 25th August 1855 there appeared the following advertisement:– "*Baker Lane Foundry, King's Lynn. Alfred Dodman, Engineer, Iron & Brass Founder, respectfully informs the owners of steam machinery that he has lately added to his stock and can supply on the shortest notice gutta-percha driving bands, gauge glasses, india-rubber rings, suction pipes, whistles, cocks, perforated plates and all requirements for this class of machinery. Engines repaired and new fireboxes on the shortest notice*".

His lease would have terminated in 1864 and it was probably then that he moved to part of the site of the former St. James Workhouse in what is now County Court Road. It had been vacant since the collapse of the tower on 20th August 1854 and had been used by Frederick Savage as the premises of his works between 1856 and 1860. The business expanded.

On 12th May 1869 Dodman applied to the Borough Treasurer for the hire of a piece of unenclosed ground at the back of his machine works at St. James place on the east side of the premises.

In 1873 he negotiated with the Borough Surveyor to supply to the Sanitary Board a new iron tank on wheels for the removal of night soil. In other words, an Ordure Cart. Also in this year two traction engines of his make were used in testing the newly-erected girder bridge spanning the Great Ouse River.

A year later in 1874 he was elected a Councillor for the South Ward and remained a Councillor until 1889.

After establishment in Lynn, Alfred Dodman had married Miss Mary Elizabeth Slator, a sister of the late J. W. Slator, an engineer, also of Lynn, but there was no legal issue. Mrs. Dodman was a director in the published list of directors contained in the Articles of Association dated 1897, when the firm's title became Alfred Dodman & Co. Ltd. Alfred Henry Crisp was Company secretary. The Company's capital was £14,000 divided into 2,800 shares of £5 each.

In 1875, as the Trustees of St. Nicholas Warden's Estates leased to Alfred Dodman for 21 years a garden of 1 acre, 2 rods, 2 perches in Gaywood Road adjacent to Highgate Bridge and the Dock Railway. He moved there and called these new premises Highgate Works.

On 8th December 1897, when the firm became Alfred Dodman & Co. Ltd., a certain James Smith was also a director and described as Secretary but was probably only at the London Office. Other directors were Charles Cousins of Lincoln, Charles Duckering of Lincoln and William Neale Turner of Ipswich, (all described as "Engineers").

The firm was placed on Army Contracts List on 8th

May 1902, on the Admiralty List on 10th June that year and on the Crown Agents for the Colonies List on 28th August 1905, for the supply of land and marine boilers.

Alfred Dodman died on 13th December 1908 at his house in London Road, Swaffham after suffering from a kidney complaint. He was a JP for the County of Norfolk, Member of the Norfolk Court of Sewers, one of the King's Lynn Municipal Trustees and recently elected chairman of that body succeeding the late T. E. Bagge of Gaywood Hall. He was buried on 18th December at Tichwell.

Probate was granted to his will on 9th February 1909. He left £21,883 18s 8d, no small fortune at that time, the chief beneficiaries being his wife who took a life interest in his shares and investments and Alfred Henry Crisp who, subject to his still holding a position in the company, was to inherit 1,000 of the shares of the company on the death of Mrs. Dodman. Another legacy was £300 to the West Norfolk and Lynn Hospitals.

Alfred Crisp took his father's christian name and his mother's surname.

The company prospered under Crisp's management up to his death in 1936. In 1931 Dodmans took over the business of E. S. Hindley & Sons of Bourton, Dorset and so acquired manufacturing rights of the Hindley high-speed totally enclosed forced lubricated steam engines suitable for a variety of applications. E. S. Hindley & Co. were established by one Daniel Maggs in c1750 as a water powered linen mill. These premises were acquired later in the next century by E. S. Hindley, an inventive engineer, and it was after his death that the goodwill and rights went to Lynn.

After Crisp's death Robert Forster took over the company which maintained its manufacturers.

In 1972 the firm changed its title to Dodman Engineering Limited to try and modernise or up-grade its image but a lack of cash flow compelled it to cease trading in February 1975. They had continued as tenants of the Trustees of St. Nicholas Warden's Estates until 1955 when they bought the freehold and remained there until the closure in 1975. Later, the site was sold to West Norfolk County Council and most of the plant to Bead Engineering in North Lynn. Bead had been established by some former employees of Dodmans and had taken away much of the old firm's business.

Curiously, the firm took out only one successful Patent, viz. No 3042 of 12th May 1881 in the names of Alfred Dodman & Nathan Gold Kimberley of Stoke Newington for "Improvements in Band Saw Machines".

It is difficult after more than a century to ascertain with certainty what type Alfred Dodman's first steam engine really was, but drawings dated 1868 indicate a portable engine. At the same time drawings were made

of repaired parts for a railway locomotive but of unknown make and type.

But undoubtedly the earliest surviving engine record is the beautifully executed drawing shown in Fig 146, depicting the complete arrangement of a small marine capstan, engine and boiler and which may be dated c1865. The engine is an inverted vee twin with duplex cylinders. As the cylinders were at 90° the engine would start with the crank in any position. It may not have been apparent at this period but such an engine was perfectly balanced for primary and secondary forces. It is interesting to note that several modern motorcycle engines have cylinders at 90° for this reason. In the Dodman example there would be a slight secondary couple due to the big-ends being side by side. Several of these capstans were made for sailing fishing smacks at this time which would facilitate mooring in confined places. The writer can remember smacks having a capstan, always noticeable because of the slanting top end of the chimney appearing above deck. Note the firm was then just plain ALFRED DODMAN ENGINEER, the word Engineer being in Black Letter.

In 1872 the first traction engine appeared, illustrated in Fig 147. Here the single cylinder 8in x 10in is placed over the firebox and the working pressure was 100 psi. The differential was carried on the second motion shaft and was placed just in front of the firebox and under the boiler barrel and on each end of the shaft was mounted a pinion engaging with a large toothed annulus bolted to the inside rings of the rear wheels. Primary drive, as will be seen, was by chain with the jockey pulley for tensioning. Front pillar steerage was used and a decorated handrail – a nice piece of blacksmith's work – was fitted part of the way round the manstand. The gross weight was about 5½ tons.

In Fig 148 we have a reproduction of an outline drawing of an early Dodman chain engine so accurately drawn that many of the items could be scaled in the shops to provide dimensions of several parts. The original, although somewhat damaged, is beautifully finished in colour wash and is of the same standard of draughtsmanship as Fig 146.

The annular drive for these engines is clearly illustrated in Fig 149 where again the original is a finely coloured wash drawing. The teeth are most accurately drawn, and the notes are written in copybook style.

Fig 146 (facing page) Exquisite drawing of Alfred Dodman's inverted vee twin capstan.

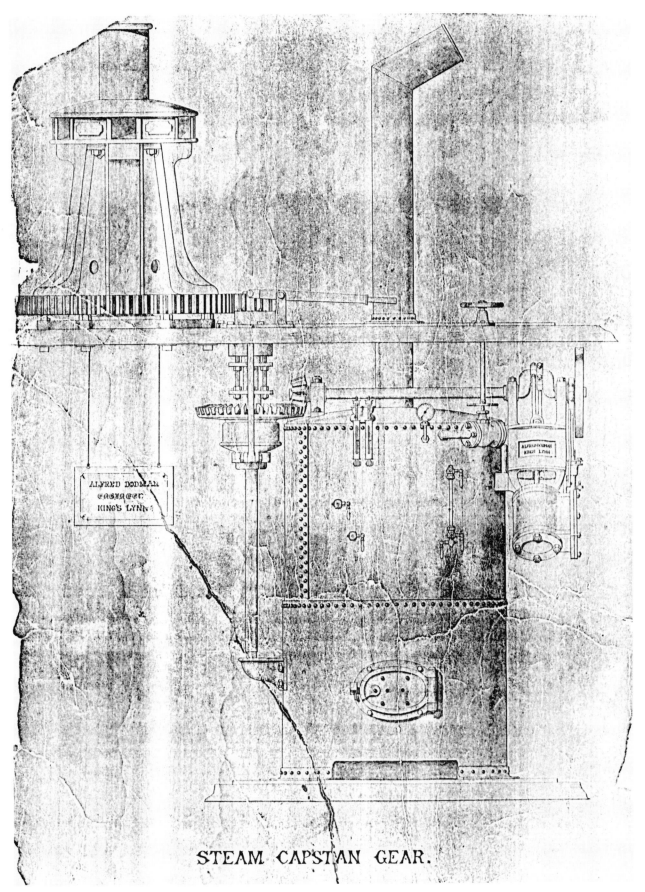

STEAM CAPSTAN GEAR.

95

Fig 147 (above) Alfred Dodman's first traction engine of 1872.
Fig 148 (below) Original drawing for the 1872 road engine.

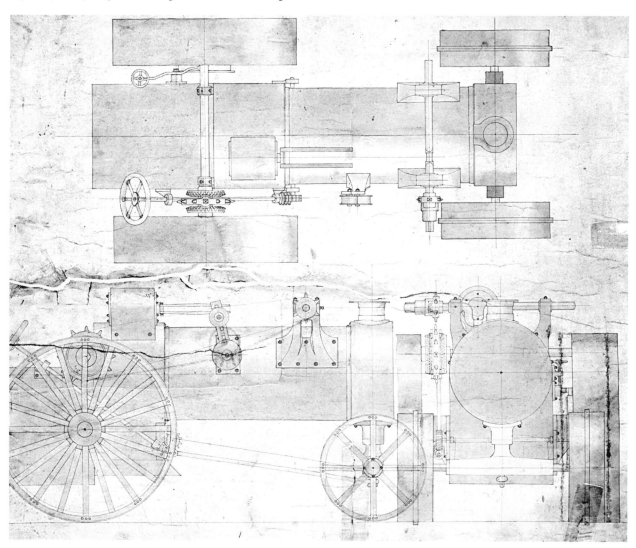

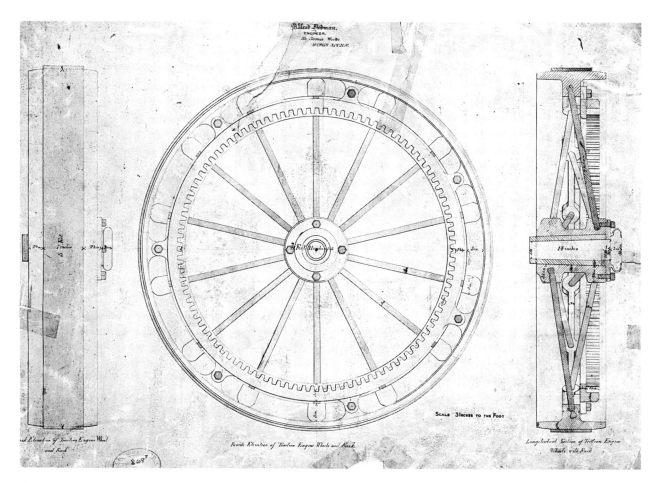

Fig 149 (above) Annular drive for the engine in Fig 147.

Fig 150 (below) First geared traction engine from Highgate Works.

In Fig 150 is shown the Dodman first geared engine produced in 1882. The drive is now through four shafts with the crankshaft pinions outside the hornplate, but the final drive gear is still an annulus on the offside driving wheel, the nearside wheel being driven by the usual withdrawable pin although there was a differential on the third shaft. The higher and more commodious tender and flywheel with curved spokes make the whole engine good-looking and picturesque. Needless to say the finish was of a very high order.

Details of the cylinder block for these engines is included in Fig 151 where the crosshead guides are formed of four bars, similar to the Burrell system. I should mention that the projections used in this drawing do not conform completely to current practice as a certain amount of licence has been taken by the draughtsman. But at this period the sole object was to illustrate and clarify as much as possible in one view and then draughtsmen used their own individual methods, a point one has to look out for when reading

Fig 152 The later geared Dodman traction engine.

Fig 151 Cylinder block for the first geared Dodman road engines.

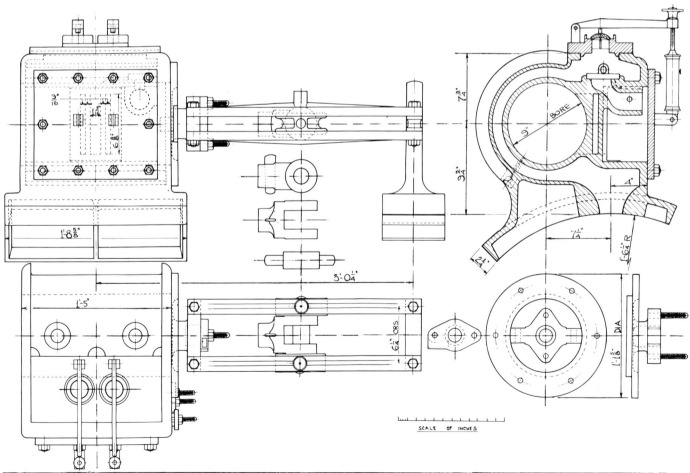

COPYRIGHT
RONALD H. CLARK A.M.I.MECH.E
DIAMOND COTTAGE
SHOTESHAM ALL SAINTS
NORWICH

early drawings. In this case the cylinder was standard for the period, the bore and stroke being 9in x 12in.

A later design of geared road engine made at the Highgate Works is illustrated in Fig 152. This represents No 2073 after testing and painting, ready in the work's yard for despatch. Little is recorded about the colours; some of these engines were painted but it is known that No 2275 left the works resplendent in royal blue.

In 1904 the 7 nhp cylinder block was simplified to the form shown in Fig 153 having a bore and stroke of 8½in x 12in. Note the smooth easy curve of the steam passage from the governor valve to the valve chest. Inlet ports were ½in wide, the exhaust 1¼in and all three were 6½in long, ensuring an easy exhaust flow.

Like his neighbour, Alfred Dodman produced a tandem compound road locomotive with cylinders 6in and 11in x 12in. Unfortunately no photograph has survived showing this interesting engine but the four views in the drawing in Fig 154 should indicate its main features. There were three speeds in the four shaft transmission and it was spring mounted. Being single geared on the last motion it had the winding drum on the rear axle. Only one example of this tandem single crank compound was made.

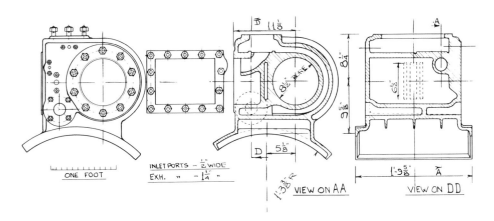

Fig 153 The 1904 design of Dodman cylinder block.

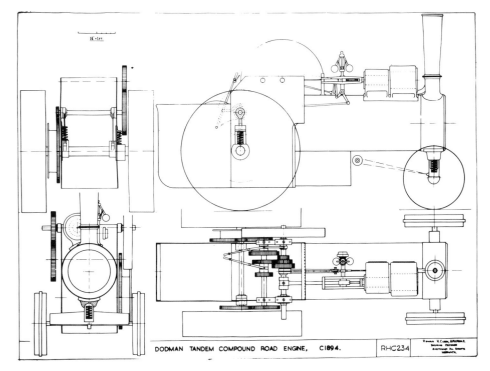

DODMAN TANDEM COMPOUND ROAD ENGINE, C1894.   RHC234

Fig 154 Four views of Dodman's tandem compound road engine.

Another Dodman single crank compound is outlined in the drawing in Fig 155 where like some other makers, Dodman was influenced towards the single crank compound type by Frederick Burrell's successful Patent of 1889 which we have considered previously. In this example Alfred Dodman placed his high pressure cylinder perpendicularly over the low pressure, presumably to side-track Burrell's arrangement. Further to avoid copying the Thetford design, Dodman, instead of employing two slide valves, designed the tall double cavity valve shown in the cylinder details in Fig 156. Here the steam entered the high pressure in the usual way but exhausted through the valve direct on to the low pressure inlet ports, its exhaust being in the orthodox manner. The cylinders were 6¼in and 11in x 12in and it will be noticed the complete engine has quite pleasing outlines. Note there are four longitudinal ties connecting the tube-plates instead of the more conventional pair. The front axle was of wood and reinforced. One example of this type was exhibited at the Cambridge RA Show in June 1894 where it seems Charles Burrell took exception to it on the grounds of similarity, so no others were made.

However, Highgate Works had another attempt at a single crank compound as will be seen from the four views in Fig 157, where the high pressure cylinder was merely moved to the horizontal on the same centreline as the low pressure. Quite an ingenious retort to Thetford!

Here the cylinders were 6in and 10½in x 12in, and four shafts in the transmission. As in the previous engine, one large slide valve only was fitted, the high pressure steam again passing through the valve on its way to the low pressure inlets. As will be seen from the plan view, this valve was operated by Stephenson's Link Motion via an overhead rocker shaft. Owing to a disastrous fire at the works between the wars, further details are unhappily not existing but I was informed by the late Mr. Crisp that it is doubtful if an engine with this cylinder block was ever made. If one was put in hand, that would be the only example.

Many of these two-speed engines could be delivered with this firm's slow motion gear, which differed from their competitors at St. Nicholas Works, for whereas Savage mounted the stud eccentrically, Dodman formed a slot in the hornplate along which the stud, – and the pinions with it – were slid in and out of gear. The drawing in Fig 158 should make the arrangement quite clear. The mathematical treatment given when dealing with the Savage gear will similarly apply in this case.

Fig 155 Alternative arrangement of Dodman's single crank compound.

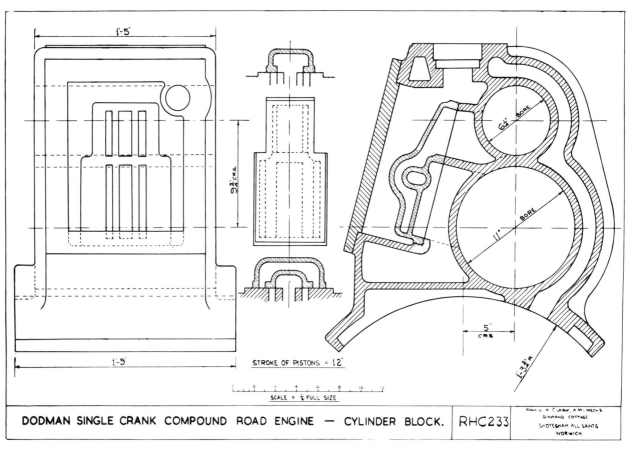

SCALE = ⅛ FULL SIZE

DODMAN SINGLE CRANK COMPOUND ROAD ENGINE — CYLINDER BLOCK. RHC233

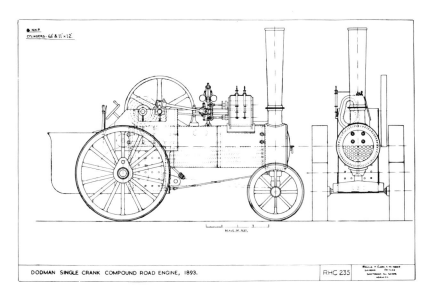

Fig 156 Offside view of the engine in Fig 155.

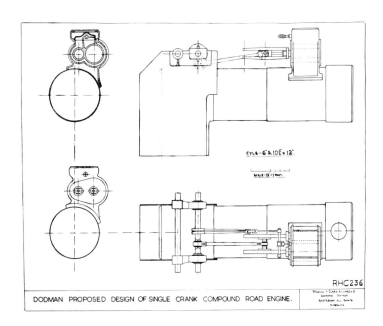

Fig 157 Another single crank compound block from Highgate Works.

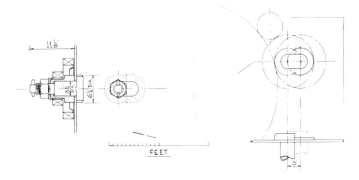

Fig 158 Slow motion gear for Dodman traction engines.

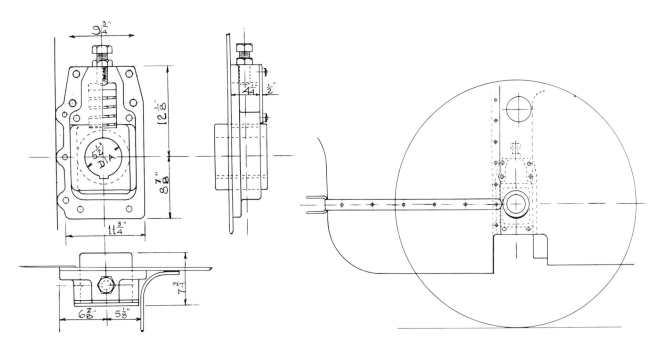

Fig 159 Dodman's rear road engine springing.

As with many other makers, Highgate Works could supply a road engine spring-mounted and their design is to be seen in Fig 159, where the axlebox moves under the action of the square section coil spring above it. Adjustment for equal loading on each rear wheel was made by the lock-nutted set screw above the spring. The rear axle blocks were keyed to the fixed axle, the engine being double-geared on the last motion but sufficient end play was allowed for during erection to permit one end of the axle to oscillate independently of the other without any jamming. The permitted vertical movement varied between ⅜in to ½in, just enough to smooth out the worst road shocks. Incidentally, all spring gears adjustment is immensely facilitated if the rear of the engine be jacked up with the rear wheels clear of the ground.

In Fig 160 are views on the gearing of No 2275 giving a clear picture of how the two road speeds were arranged with the change speed levers controlled from the manstand.

Dodman's final design of single cylinder block is illustrated in Fig 161 and was used on all their later road engines and on several portables. To ensure a leak-proof joint between the cylinder and boiler, a separate cast iron base or seating was permanently riveted to the shell and the cylinder block bolted on as will be seen in the drawing. A 1½in Gas filler plug is fitted to the top right hand curve of the steam jacket and water heater steam was taken from the exhaust chamber. The original sketches of this design are dated 9th June 1910.

Fig 160 Two-speed transmission gearing on Dodman engine No 2275.

The general arrangement drawing reproduced in Fig 162 will show how the details in Fig 161 were incorporated into the completed design and this should

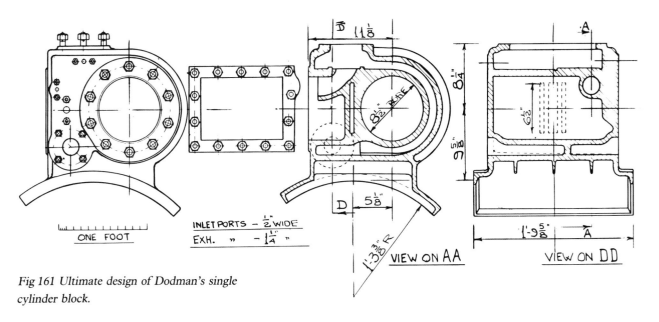

ONE FOOT

INLET PORTS - ½" WIDE
EXH. " - 1¼" "

VIEW ON AA

VIEW ON DD

*Fig 161 Ultimate design of Dodman's single
cylinder block.*

BRAKE HORSE POWER	30
CYLINDER - BORE	8½"
" - STROKE	12"
FLYWHEEL - DIAMETER	4'-6"
R.P.M.	155
DRIVING WHEELS - DIAMETER	5'-11½"
" " - WIDTH	16"
LENGTH OVERALL	16'-9"
WIDTH "	7'-4"
HEIGHT TO TOP OF FLYWHEEL	8'-10"
ROAD SPEEDS - M.P.H.	2 & 4

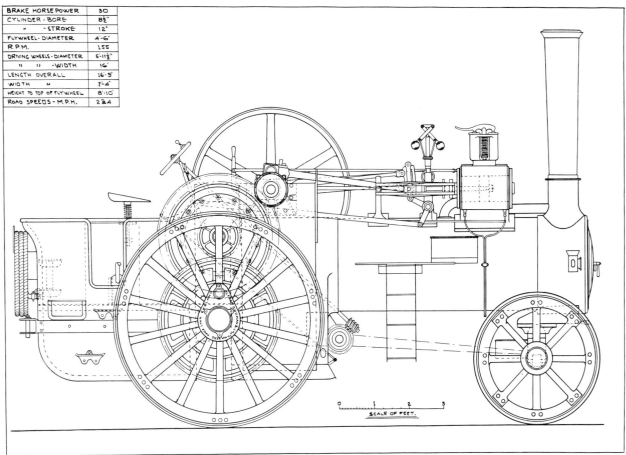

SCALE OF FEET.

Fig 162 General arrangement of Dodman's last design of road engine.

be studied in conjunction with the photograph in Fig 152. An offside view of a road engine of the above class is included in Fig 163 which was exhibited at a local agricultural show in 1911 and was bought direct

from the showground. By 1940 it was still working with its original firebox.

To keep abreast of current practice and to compete with other firms, the Highgate work's drawing office in

Fig 163 A late-type general purpose traction engine from
Highgate Works.

Fig 164 Dodman's five ton tractor and gearing.

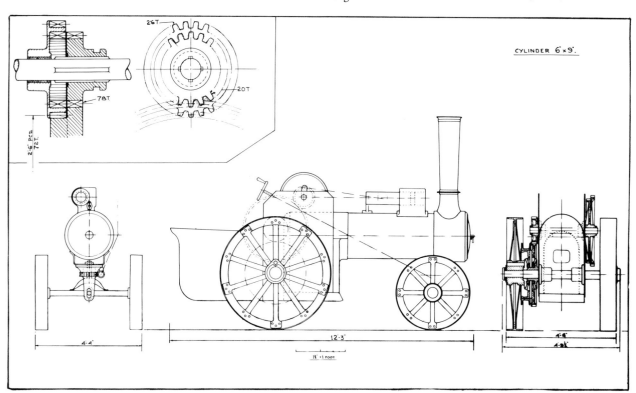

1904 produced a design for a small road engine to comply with the requirements of the Heavy Motor Car Orders of 1903, and such engines as we have seen were classed as Steam Motor Tractors. It was a light engine of less than 5 tons unladen and its outline is shown in Fig 164. It had two very interesting features. One was the worm and wormwheel steering detailed in the front end view and the other was the gearing, more clearly seen in the enlarged detail. The high speed crankshaft pinion was free to revolve on the shaft and ran on a gunmetal bush. It had internal as well as external teeth. The low speed wheel was always splined to, and therefore always rotated with, the crankshaft. When meshed with the larger toothed ring in the spur-ring we have low gear. When moved free of it and into the internal teeth in the high speed pinion, both pinions thus ran round together and as the high speed was always in mesh with the smaller or high speed ring, we have high speed. For neutral the low speed pinion was moved to the right and clear of the high speed pinion and spur-ring. The great advantage was that only one hand lever was required and the two ratios could not both be engaged at the same time. There were 26T in the high speed and 20T in the low speed pinions, with 72T and 78T corresponding in the spur-rings. The two ratios were therefore 2·75 and 3·9 : 1. The final drive as will be seen from the back axle section, was single geared in the last motion at 2½ : 1, so that the overall ratios were 7 and 9¾ : 1. As the legal permitted speeds were 5 mph for tractors on light haulage, these ratios would be about right. Other main dimensions were:–

Cylinder	6in x 9in
Height to top of chimney	8ft 6¾in
Width over front wheels	4ft 4in
Width over rear wheels	4ft 6in
Width over hub caps	4ft 9½in
Length overall	12ft 3in

From the scant records remaining it seems that unfortunately only one of these interesting little tractors was made and the customer is unkown.

What one may term a natural derivative from the traction engine is the Traction Tram Engine where the basis of the design is a traction engine but adapted to run on four or more flanged wheels on a tramway. In Fig 165 are illustrated four types of Dodman traction tram engines, the left-hand engine being of the 2–4–0 wheel arrangement with the cylinders and motion mounted on the under-framing. Instead of four coupled driving wheels a pair of large traction engine flanged wheels could be used as shown by the dotted circle, making it a 2–2–0 engine. In the right-hand view the cylinder is mounted on the boiler as on a road engine

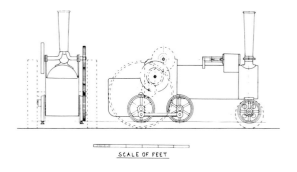

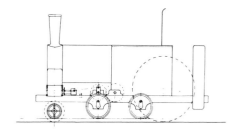

Fig 165 Traction tram engine, undermounted, by Alfred Dodman.

and with four shafts in the transmission making it a 2–4–0. Here again a single pair of traction engine-type rear wheels could be used. Note all four had only one speed in the geared transmission. Unfortunately, there are few surviving records of these engines so it is not now clear how many were made and who were the customers.

It is always interesting and absorbing to study designs of steam engines which were never made, and the Dodman steam motor wagon is in this category. The drawings are dated 28th January 1914 and from Mr. Crisp I gathered that because of a full order book that year, and then the onset of the war itself, a complete wagon was never made. In Fig 166 we have a nearside prospect and a front end view from which it will be seen that it had a pleasing outline, being well proportioned and with a large area available for the payload. Note that the firm's title on the smokebox door ring is simply DODMAN LTD. The principal dimensions were:–

Length of platform	12ft 0in
Width of platform	7ft 0in
Rear wheels, diameter	3ft 6in
Rear wheels, width	10in
Front wheels, diameter	2ft 9in
Front wheels, width	6in
Height to top of chimney	9ft 4in
Length overall	22ft 0in
Width overall	7ft 0in

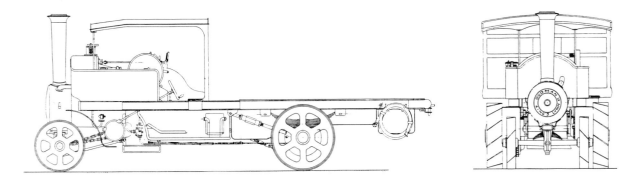

Fig 166 Outline drawing of the Dodman 5 ton steam wagon.

There were two speeds in the gearing and the differential was mounted within the rear axle chain sprocket. Note also the steerage worm and wheel neatly enclosed.

Fig 167 illustrates the main details of the motion gear and compound cylinder block, the cylinders being 4in and 6½in x 7in spaced at 8in centres. Steam to each cylinder was controlled by a piston valve, both valves were 3in diameter. With such valves the inlet ports are short and straight, thus eliminating any wire-drawing due to the usual double curved ports used with slide valves, and giving a very free steam flow. A 3-way plug cock could close the low pressure cylinder to exhaust from the high pressure and allow high pressure boiler steam to enter, thus making the engine "double-high" at will. In conjunction with the 3-way cock the piston

Fig 167 Cylinder and motion details of the Dodman steam wagon.

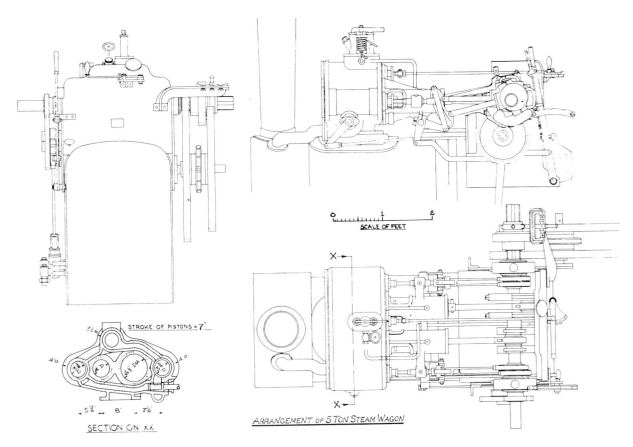

106

starting valve had to be moved a little further forward to close the ordinary inlet port and open a further one, letting high pressure steam only to the low pressure cylinder as well as to the high pressure. When working double-high there would, of course, be four staccato beats per revolution. The starting piston valve was 2½in diameter. It was for the period, 1914, a very advanced design and it is regrettable that the forthcoming war put an end to manufacture and further development.

It is not recorded which was the first portable engine made and its date but undoubtedly such engines were available from the early days of the firm. A good example is seen in Fig 168 with the typical short boiler of large diameter. No working pressure is stated but it was probably 80 psi and the fireboxes were all of Lowmoor Iron. They were to be had in powers of 2½, 3, 4, 5, 6, 7, 8, 10 and 12 nhp. The smallest engine ran at 150 and the two larger at 110 rpm. They were described as being "*well adapted for the use of landed proprietors, Agriculturists and Brickmakers*", and the 2½ nhp would cost the buyer £98 and the 12 nhp an even £250. Although a mechanical feed pump is included, one would have an additional and stand-by Hand Force Pump as seen in the illustration, just to make sure as it were.

ALFRED DODMAN'S
IMPROVED PORTABLE
STEAM ENGINES.

Fig 168 An early Dodman portable with a single cylinder.

If more bhp was required there were the duplex portables, one of which is depicted in Fig 169. Their specification was similar to that of the single cylinder engines but the nhp ranged from 8 to 40, the last named having a flywheel no less than 7 feet diameter. Like many other makes, the Dodman product could be had with enlarged fireboxes for burning wood, straw, stalks,

etc. where such combustible rubbish was surplus for fuel.

The later and last type of portable is shown in Fig 170 where the general outline is very pleasing and for the period 1900–1910, equal to any other made. The smaller sizes have been dropped, the smallest now being of 4 and the largest, 14 nhp. The working pressure was now 100 psi and hydraulically tested to 180 psi. Many were exported.

Fig 169 Duplex cylinders on a Dodman early portable.

Fig 170 Late type of Dodman portable.

Portable & Semi-Portable
Steam Engines.

Next comes the well-known overtype where in place of wheels and axles the boiler and motion were mounted on a heavy cast iron ashpan and cast iron smokebox support. Again the sizes were exactly as for the portables.

Curiously, the Highgate Works undertype worked at the odd pressure of 90 psi and was available in three Classes – B, C and F. Class B was the simplest form having only a Pickering governor but Class C, shown in Fig 171 had a governor of the Hartnell type controlling the travel of the slide valve – a form of expansion regulator whereby the cut-off was automatically suited to the load. A much more economical method than by throttling the steam. All the classes had a common foundation or base formed of a girder frame of rolled steel joists and the smokebox was supported on a cast iron saddle above the cylinder. Class F was more refined, having Stephenson's link motion reversing gear. All three classes were made in from 3 to 14 nhp sizes, the first indicating 17 ihp, the 10, 45 and the 14, 69 ihp. These figures were obtained with 90 psi in the steam chest and cut-off at half stroke. As such engines required only simple foundations and were easily fixed, many were made for export where simplicity was necessary.

HIGH PRESSURE UNDER TYPE ENGINES

SINGLE CYLINDER.

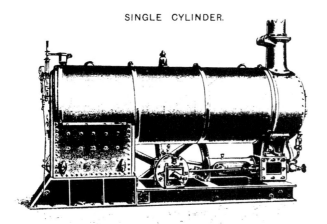

Fig 171 An undertype from Highgate Works.

At one time Highgate works were renowned for their variety of horizontal fixed engines, a customer having a choice of no less than ten or more designs. The very impressive tandem compound is illustrated in Fig 172 showing the 40 nhp engine having cylinders 14in and 24in x 30in. Some idea of the size can be estimated by the erector standing at the starting valve. At the rear is a jet condenser. Their normal rpm was 80 and they were listed at £495. For another £30 extra a shaft governor could be fitted regulating the cut-off to suit the load. The smallest was of 12 nhp with cylinders 8in and 14in x 16in and the largest 50 nhp having cylinders 16in and 27in x 36 in. This last named was probably the largest horizontal engine made in Norfolk.

Two smaller engines with tandem cylinders and rated at 8 and 10 nhp were produced where the cylinder scaled 6in and 10in x 14in and 7in and 12in x 14in respectively. These two engines, however, were of slightly different design, being mounted on a brick or masonry bed seen in Fig 173.

A favourite form of compound horizontal was the cross-coupled type and the Dodman engine is depicted in Fig 174 where the jet condenser is in tandem with and behind the low pressure clearly seen in the illustration. For certain working conditions a surface condenser could be supplied. There were eight different sizes in the whole range of 12 to 50 nhp where in all cases the working pressure was now 100 psi. The 12 and 50 nhp engines had cylinders of the same dimensions as those in Fig 172. This range was quite costly, the largest being priced at £675.

Fig 172 A tandem compound horizontal by Alfred Dodman.

TANDEM COMPOUND ENGINES.

GIRDER TYPE BEDS. CONDENSING OR NON CONDENSING.

Where a cheaper and smaller tandem compound was required, it took the form illustrated in Fig 175, showing a non-condensing engine. Although cheaper, it could have the refinement of a Meyer expansion valve working on the back of the main slide valve and which could be adjusted while the engine was running. Alternatively, the Meyer valve could be controlled automatically by a shaft governor. The range of powers was medium and from 12 to 30 nhp, the intermediate sizes being 16, 20 and 25 nhp.

Fig 173 Another example of a small Dodman tandem compound horizontal engine.

CROSS COMPOUND ENGINES.

GIRDER TYPE BEDS.   WITH OR WITHOUT CONDENSORS.

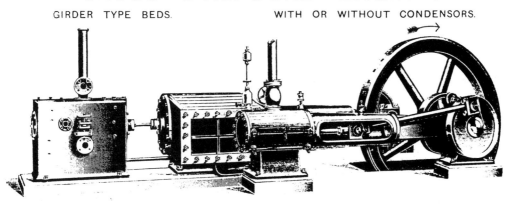

Fig 174 A cross-coupled compound from Highgate Works, Lynn.

COMPOUND STEAM ENGINES.

Tandem No. 4 Design.   Condensing if required.

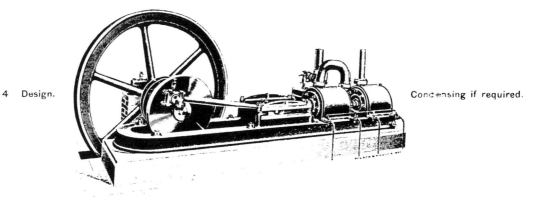

Fig 175 A horizontal with tandem compound cylinders.

Fig 176 An alternative horizontal with a single cylinder.

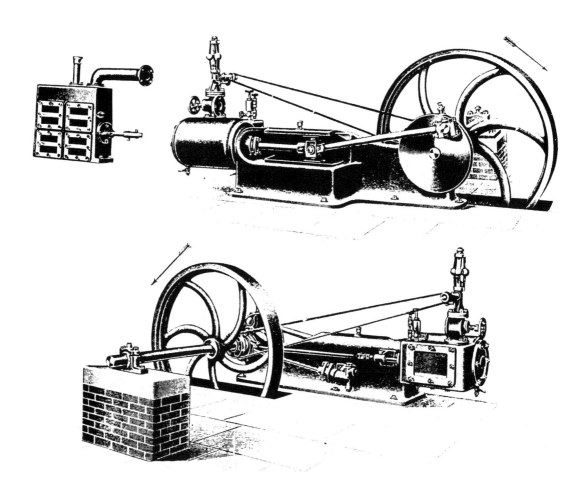

Fig 177 A horizontal Dodman engine with the cylinder cantilevered.

A feature extolled by the makers and possessed by the smaller engine in Fig 176 was that the foundation, front cylinder cover, guide-bars and main crankshaft bearing are all in one casting and cored out where necessary. This permitted the crosshead guide, and front cover for fixing the cylinder to be machined at one setting, thus ensuring correct alignment of cylinder, frame and crankshaft. The cylinder covers, crankshaft and connecting rod were turned bright thus having a very fine finish. Class B had a Pickering and Class C a shaft governor as in some previous engines. Again, the standard ratings were used of 8 to 25 nhp, the respective cylinders being 9in x 18in and 16in x 30in. As will be seen from Fig 175 a tandem compound could be provided, if desired.

Another simple design of horizontal had the single cylinder cantilevered beyond the end of the cast iron foundation casting and Fig 177 clearly illustrates the layout. They were intended for the user requiring only a small handy engine so the smallest of 1½ nhp had a cylinder only 4in x 6in and the 2 nhp 4¾in x 7in but the largest of 20 nhp in the range had its cylinder 14in x 20in. As in the previous design the main framing was cast and machined in one unit ensuring correct alignment of the cylinder, crosshead guides and crankshaft. These engines had to be sold in a very competitive market and the list price of the 1½ nhp size was only £28.

In Fig 178 we have a straightforward design of a simple cross-coupled engine with duplex cylinders, disc cranks and trunk or bored guides. They were made in the same sizes and powers as the previous engines and with both cylinders taking boiler steam. With their

cranks at 90° they would start in any position. An alternative design had top and bottom guides to each crosshead. As seen in the illustration the steam pipes were bare but after erection they would be heavily lagged.

Yet another variety of horizontal engine was available for the customer of those days and this had a form of cast iron frame, easily traced in the view of Fig 179. Every working part was readily accessible and engines could be had in four sizes of 6, 8, 10 and 14 nhp, the corresponding cylinders being 7½in x 12in, 8¼in x 12in, 10in x 14in and 12in x 14in. They were relatively slow speed when the normal rpm of the 24 nhp was 125. A number of this class were used for belt driving electric generators and for this job the shaft governor was preferred.

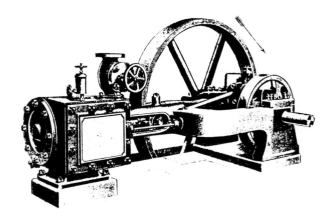

Fig 179 The double girder bed type of horizontal.

Vertical cross-coupled compound engines were another type produced at Highgate Works and a good example is to be seen in Fig 180, designed for rope driving to electric generators or any other machinery situated some distance from the engine room. For example, weaving sheds. In Fig 180 the cylinders were 6¾in and 10¾in x 9in using steam at up to 120 psi. Any engine could be made with a jet or surface condenser and with duplex cylinders, if desired. Governing could be by shaft or Porter governor and an alternative was a Meyer expansion valve where the cut-off was set by hand.

A simpler vertical was the smaller design having a single cylinder, one eccentric, and non-reversing, as may be seen in the engraving in Fig 181. They were intended for the customer who wanted a small and robust engine. The smallest was only 1½ nhp with a 4in x 6in cylinder, the largest of 16 nhp having a cylinder 13in x 18in. With a working pressure of only 70 psi the smallest developed 4½ ihp cutting off at half stroke and running at 240 rpm. All cylinders were neatly lagged

Fig 178 A duplex cross-coupled horizontal made in Lynn.

Fig 180 A Dodman vertical cross-coupled compound engine.

Fig 181 A Dodman single cylinder vertical engine.

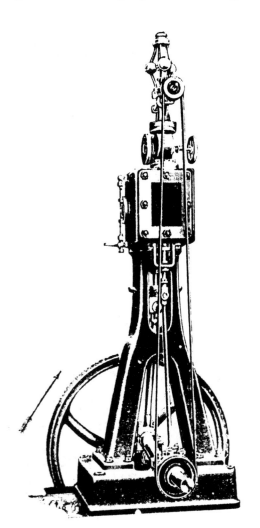

with sheet steel confined by brass bands and complete with lubricators to all bearings and drain cocks to cylinder and valve chest. A most comprehensive specification for a list price of only £23! The writer saw one of this type in a disused brewery in West Norfolk not many years ago.

To cater for the demands of civil and railway contractors at this period many steam hoists and hauling engines were supplied by Highgate Works and a typical example is depicted in Fig 182. They were designed for use in small workings, surface and underground, were self-contained and needed not expensive foundations, etc. Both drums were lined with wood or iron on cast iron cheeks and were easily removable from the shaft, especially when adjusting the length of ropes for up and down working. A powerful footbrake and reversing gear were, of course, fitted as standard. If required, a flywheel could be included to run separately from the winding gear for belt driving.

Fig 182 Dodman's winding engine with duplex cylinders.

Four powers were available with cylinders 5in x 7in, 6in x 8in, 6½ x 10in and 7in x 10in.

A very compact and charming, if one may use the word in considering a steam hoist, single cylinder winder is included in Fig 183. The engine proper was erected on a wrought iron box foundation or frame not requiring an elaborate preparation. Four sizes were given in terms of cylinder bores, these being 8in x 14in, 9in x 16in, 10in x 20in and 11in x 20in and all took steam at 80 psi to suit the firm's complementary vertical boiler, all of which worked at this pressure which appeared to be a national standard. The 8in x 14in hoist cost £113 complete. If required, the cylinders could be arranged cross-coupled with the drum between them, their size being as for the single cylinder machine. The 8in x 14in single cylinder hoist was listed at £123 and the 11in x 20in duplex at £310. These prices included all the foundation nuts bolts and so on but not the ropes, although these could be supplied, if required.

necessary steady running. Cylinder covers were finished bright and polished and lagging sheeting quality painted to match a generally high standard of finish. Note the three bearing crankshaft; a fourth or outrigger bearing could be supplied at a slight extra cost.

Fig 183 A Lynn winding engine with a single cylinder.

On many civil engineering sites it was an advantage for a power plant to be portable and so we find in Fig 184 a self-contained hoisting unit with all parts mounted on a steel frame and with a swivelling front bogie. They were used in dock and other warehouses, by builders, for pile driving and the vertical cross tube boiler could burn most scrap combustible material. The engraving shows the main details very clearly but note the flywheel just behind the engine. With the drum clutched out of gear the user had a vertical engine for any other purpose. They were made in 2, 3, 4, 5, 6 and 8 nhp sizes, the cylinder dimensions were as for the previous engines of these powers and the gearing was of best quality close grained cast iron.

An exceptionally neat and good looking compound vertical engine is shown in Fig 185 and there were eight different nhp's in the range of from 10 to 35. The smallest, 10 nhp, would develop 17 ihp when using steam at 140 psi, running at 260 rpm and having cylinders 5in and 9in x 8in. Many were used for electric lighting and when a shaft governor was fitted for the

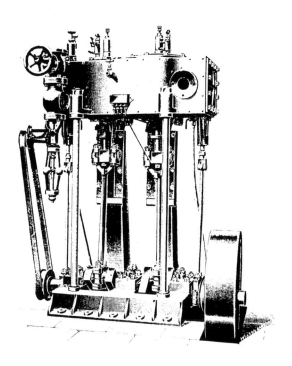

Fig 185 Vertical compound Dodman engine.

Fig 184 Dodman's portable vertical hoisting engine.

It is but a short step in design from a successful vertical stationary engine to a marine version and Alfred Dodman was not lacking when it came to meeting a demand for engines for the smaller pleasure steamer and coasters. A typical and picturesque example is illustrated in Fig 186 having compound cylinders supported on the port side by cast iron columns in which are formed the slipper crosshead guides with the starboard side supported on bright steel columns, all mounted on a base sole plate of box or rib section with the square recesses for the main shaft bearings. Reversing was by Stephenson's link motion via a hand lever clearly seen in the illustration, but for the larger sizes a screw and wheel was provided. Usually, the surface condenser formed part of the framing as shown and fitted with brass tubes and tubeplates. A single-acting air pump was operated by levers off the crosshead.

This interesting range included engines from 20 ihp to 220 ihp, the smallest having cylinders 5in and 9in x 8in and the 220 ihp 14in and 28in x 18in, all using steam at 140 psi. As propeller diameters naturally varied according to the size of the vessel, their speeds would vary so, instead of any speeds being given in rpm, the recommended rate was a piston speed of 350 fpm and the rpm thereon dependent.

All were beautifully finished with many being supplied to the Admiralty. Cylinder covers were finished bright and polished, the cylinders were lagged with fitted mahogany strips, also polished, and secured by polished brass bands. Painting was to customer's requirements. I consider an engine of this type a charming subject for the model maker.

At one period the steam launch was a common sight on many main rivers and the Broadland areas, a number being privately owned. For their propulsion a small high speed marine engine was developed to power not only launches, but Admiralty pinnaces. In Fig 187 we have a little launch engine of 2 nhp having a cylinder 4in x 5½in and priced at £40 complete with feed pump. Extras were such items as stern gear, tube, propeller and sea cocks etc. In this design the cylinder was supported on a cast iron back standard with a bright turned and polished column in front, and lagged with felt, polished mahogany and brass bands, together with all necessary fittings such as drain cocks, oil box and pipes.

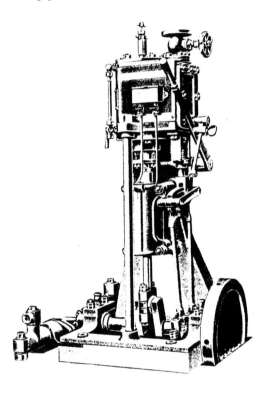

Fig 187 *The neat single cylinder launch engine from Highgate Works.*

Fig 188 *A Dodman launch engine with duplex cylinders and boiler.*

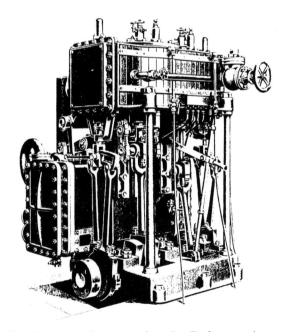

Fig 186 *A vertical compound marine Dodman engine.*

A variation was the 4 nhp launch engine with duplex cylinders, in reality a doubling-up of the single cylinder version where the two cylinders were mounted on cast iron back standards and with two bright turned steel columns at the front instead of one. The smallest had cylinders 4in x 5½in up to the largest of 10 nhp with cylinders 7in x 8in. Fig 188 shows one of these duplex engines complete with a small single flue marine boiler, propeller shaft and propeller together with all necessary steam pipes and connections. Note the funnel is hinged at its base on the smokebox to permit it to be lowered when passing under bridges. Incidentally, the 4 nhp engine was listed at a mere £76.

As the steam launch and small coaster was a common sight years ago, so was the paddle steamer, of which few examples now exist. It is not surprising therefore to find Highgate Works produced a large and fine inclined compound paddle engine illustrated by the firm's working drawing in Fig 189, showing it complete with its boiler and how the set was installed in the ship. Both engine and boiler were mounted on built-up wrought iron framing, the total length of which was 42ft 5in, the side girders being 5ft 6in centres apart. The cylinders were 10in and 20in x 30in, the crankshaft 6in diameter, mounting the paddles each end. Both paddles were 9ft 0in tip diameter x 5ft 0in wide. Stephenson gear with launch-type links ensured quick reversing by the hand lever shown.

The boiler was of the marine-loco type evolved for this type of engine and vessel and was fired from the forrad end, the funnel being about amidships. This drawing is dated 27th November 1899 but unfortunately no further details have been discovered. It is certainly one of the most interesting marine engines built in the county.

Norfolk is not a county famed for its railway locomotives but Alfred Dodman's establishment was responsible for two delightful little 2-2-2 well tank engines on the design of which the drawing office started work as early as March 1892. Two engines were made; the first was completed early in 1893 and went to the West Norfolk Farmer's Chemical & Manure Works in South Lynn. Many years later it was heard of as being in Australia. The second, completed a little later, was built to the order of William Burkitt Esq. who was a director of the King's Lynn Docks & Railway established by their Act of 19th June 1865. He named it *Gazelle* and a side view is reproduced in Fig 190.

After a damaging fire at Highgate Works, many valuable drawings of some engines were lost but later a few relating to *Gazelle* came into the writer's possession. These, which may be taken as correct, of course, show some differences to what has been published and conjectured elsewhere. From the drawings the following details have been compiled:–

Gauge	4ft 8½in
Type	2–2–2
Wheels	Mansell type
Wheels Driving, dia.	3ft 9in
Wheels Leading & Trailing, dia.	2ft 3in
Wheelbase, total	10ft 6in
Cylinders, (2)	4in x 9in
Crankshaft, dia.	3in
Crankshaft, centres of cranks and of cyls.	3ft 1½in
Crankshaft overall length	5ft 5¼in
Crankshaft dia., and bore at wheel centres	3½in
Valve gear	Stephenson's
Valve travel	1½in
Horizontal centre of crankshaft to centre of expansion link	2ft 5½in
Boiler shell, outside dia.	2ft 2in
Steam dome, outside dia., x height	9in x 9⅞in
Brass dome cladding, outside dia	9⅞in
Overall height to top of safety valves above crown plate	1ft 2⅞in
Twin Salter safety valves, dia. each	1¹¹⁄₁₆in
Twin Salter safety valves, tail lever, length	7in
Smokebox door, dia.	1ft 10in
Exhaust nozzle, bore	1½in
Shell plates, thickness	⅜in
Boiler centre line above rail	3ft 11in
Weight in working order	5½ ton
Height from rail to top of chimney	7ft 9in

Being a railway director in those days had its advantages as Burkitt was able to run his engine on to the GE and M & GN Jt Railways, something which would now horrify BR. On one occasion he ran to Cambridge and back and on another to Chesterfield, returning the same day, 27th July 1897. The distance was 105 miles each way or a total run of 210 miles. He left King's Lynn at 6.10 am and arrived at Chesterfield at 11.20 having lost 50 minutes due to delays and hand tablet changing on the single track sections of the Joint. Even so and against a northerly gale the average speed

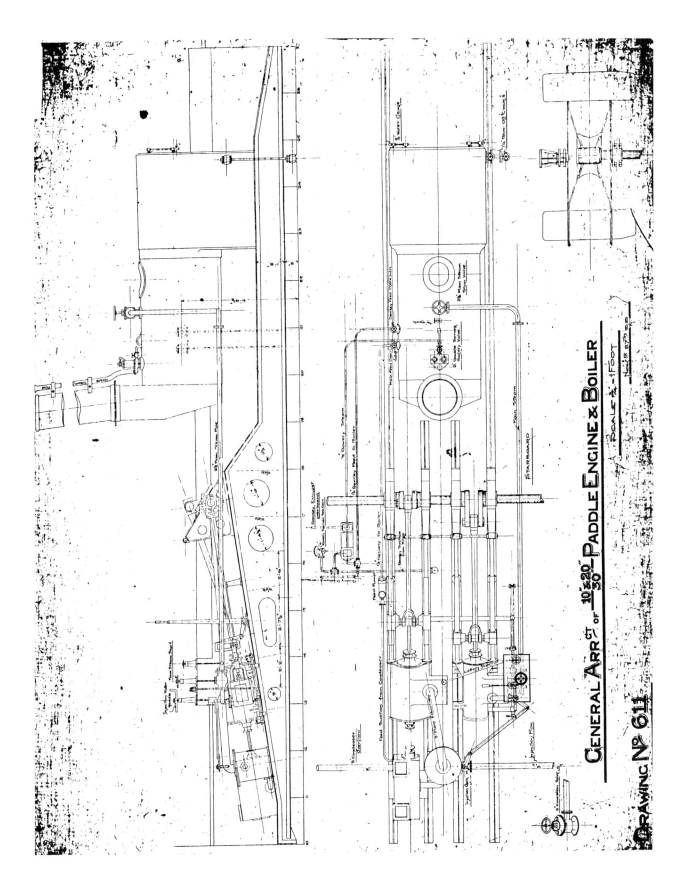

GENERAL ARR.ᵍᵗ OF 10"&20"/30" PADDLE ENGINE & BOILER

SCALE 3/4" - 1 FOOT

DRAWING Nº 611

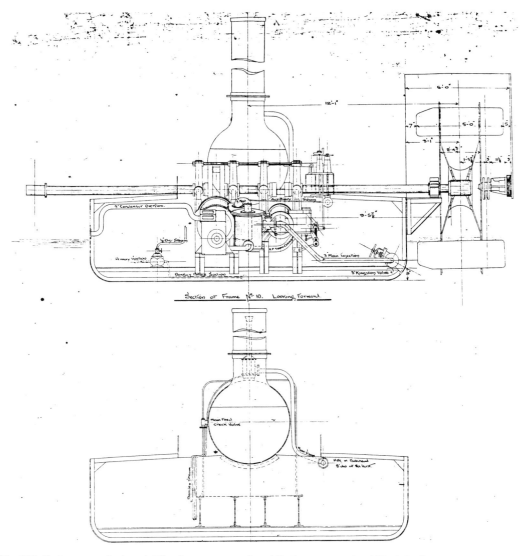

Section of Frame Nº 10.   Looking Forward

Fig 189 (facing page & above) The fine compound paddle boat engine by Alfred Dodman.

Fig 190 (below) Gazelle, Dodman's famous small railway locomotive.

was 24 mph. Returning, he left Chesterfield at 3 pm and ran into King's Lynn at 8.25 pm. The route was via Spalding and Pyewipe Junction to Lincoln and then along what was then the new branch to Chesterfield Market Station. It was driven by Burkitt's driver aided by a Joint pilotman over the Joint portions of the journey.

After Birkitt's decease, the little engine was advertised for sale in the *Locomotive Magazine* for September 1900 with a small carriage to hold four persons included. Here the wheels were referred to as "polished teak block wheels" and its maximum speed was given as 45 mph. After sale it went to the Shropshire & Montgomeryshire Light Railway in July 1911 and afterwards in their hands it had suffered an awful metamorphosis into a 0-4-2 carried out by Messrs. W. G. Bagnall Ltd at Stafford. Later it turned up on the military Longmoor Railway. By comparing the old drawings of *Gazelle* with other engine drawings by the firm it is quite obvious a number of traction and portable engine standard parts, especially where the motion is involved, were used in both engines. From an engineering and production point of view it was the obvious thing to do. Even so, the 337 rpm required to touch 45 mph is a bit rapid even for a fast road engine.

As many readers may know, *Gazelle* is now preserved in York Railway Museum where it may be seen in its final state after alterations. Birkitt's activities on two main line railways with his own private engine also serve to accentuate that he lived in far more exciting times, parallelled by the Duke of Sutherland with his famous 0-6-0 *Dunrobin*.

After acquiring the business of E. S. Hindley & Sons in 1931, Highgate Works concentrated upon both types of Hindley high speed totally-enclosed forced lubricated engines, viz. single cylinder and compound examples. In Fig 191 we have the neat single cylinder engine ranging from 1 to 100 bhp with a common working pressure of 100 psi, with corresponding speeds of 450 to 1,000 rpm. Cylinder dimensions were 3¼in x 2½in to 12in x 8in. Note for such high speeds the cylinders are now made over-square, quite unlike the slower and earlier machines. The small 1 bhp was only 36½in overall height and its other dimensions would permit it to go into a space only 25¼in x 16½in. Driven machinery could be by belt off the flywheel or direct coupled on the bedplate extended, and included fans, pumps, and generators, the last named frequently fitted aboard ships.

The Hindley compound engine is illustrated in Fig 192 showing the 200 bhp size direct coupled to a 125 KW dc generator. In this size the cylinders were 10in and 16in x 8in running at 500 rpm and were lagged with asbestos fibre and sheet metal cladded. Governing

Fig 191 The Dodman-Hindley single cylinder high speed engine.

was by a centrifugal crankshaft governor operating a balanced equilbrium throttle valve and the speed could be adjusted when running to within about 5% up or down. Speed did not vary more than 2½% from no load to full load and the momentary variation due to a shock load was not greater than 5%. True alignment of the cylinder with the crankcase was achieved by the simple expedient of using a cast iron distance piece forming the crosshead guide to which the cylinder and crankcase were spigoted.

After Highgate Works ceased manufacture of Hindley engines their production was continued by The Hindley Engine Co. Ltd. at Victoria Works, Runcorn, Cheshire.

Two views are included in Fig 193 of the old Highgate Works, one depicting the large faceplate on which were turned large flywheels and the bosses of traction engine wheels bored. Some of the columns in the long boiler shop were of timber cut from the tree trunk and the writer can remember some traces of bark visible up to recent times. Other wood columns were reputed to have been from old ship's spars. The other photograph shows part of the erecting shop.

118

Fig 192 The Dodman-Hindley compound high speed
enclosed engine.

Fig 193 A view of Highgate Works, now destroyed.

The concluding Fig 194 shows a portrait of Alfred Dodman, together with his signature and one of the firm's nameplates measuring 6in x 3½in. Today nothing remains of the old Highgate Works after exactly a century of industry and trading.

XV

HENRY ELVIN & SON,
East Green Ironworks, CASTLE ACRE.

A small village firm started by Benjamin Elvin who, in 1845, proclaimed himself as a Whitesmith, and later as an Ironfounder in 1858 and 1869. By 1888 and 1900 his son had joined him to make it as above, when their full title was Iron & Brass Founders and Agricultural Implement Makers. In their later days besides the small foundry they employed three smiths and possessed a few and varied lathes.

Like other small village firms they produced a small single cylinder portable with a traction engine-type chimney and light traction engine design of front wheels. Unfortunately little more seems to have been preserved about what must have been an interesting small country-made engine.

It is on record, however, that at this period they lengthened a traction engine by inserting an extra section in the shell and fitting a dome between the cylinder and chimney.

XVI

THE FARMER'S FOUNDRY CO. LTD.,
St. Andrew's Works, GREAT RYBURGH.

A small country works established by Percival Everitt and his friend William John Adams in 1878 who styled themselves "Everitt Adams & Co." makers of "Patent

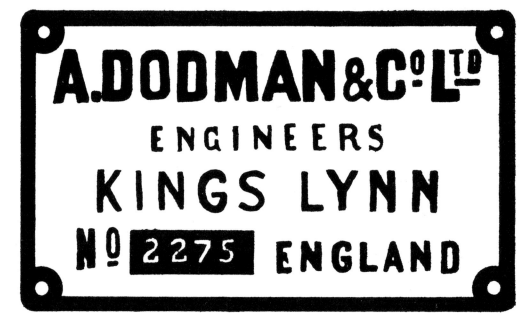

Fig 194 Alfred Dodman's signature and a nameplate.

Steam Cultivating Machinery". But an oval nameplate 12¾in x 8½in in the author's collection reads "Everitt Adams & Co. Limited, Engineers, Ryburgh, Norfolk", all in prominent Roman capitals. However the partnership was dissolved in 1880 and by 1888 the title had been changed to "The Farmer's Foundry Co. Ltd." with Thomas C. Cooper as Managing Director.

It is interesting to note that William Adams was born in 1853 in the West India Docks precincts of East London and served his time at Bow Locomotive Works. His father was none other than William Adams, the well-known locomotive engineer who was chief engineer to the North London Railway, the GER, and later the L & SWR.

After leaving Ryburgh, William junior went to the Westinghouse Co. as Manager. Later, he emigrated to Australia and in Sydney established his own firm in 1884, styled William Adams & Co. Ltd., to supply all classes of engineer's requisites. One agency in later years was that for the Sentinel Wagon Works Ltd. Ultimately, the firm was absorbed into Tubemakers, Australia Ltd. in 1984, after exactly a century of active business.

One of the first engines to be built was a light type of compound chain traction engine having cylinders 6in and 9in x 11in and four various views of its configuration can be studied from the ancient engraving reproduced in Fig 195. With the crankshaft turning over at 270 rpm the road speed was 4 mph but when belt driving agricultural machinery the governed speed was 170 rpm. This engine had several novelties, one being the disc flywheel when almost every engine at this period favoured a spoked wheel. Another was the chain, which was fabricated from stampings made from sawblade steel ¹⁄₁₆in thick and there were 32 pieces forming each side plate, the centres of the ⁷⁄₁₆in diameter pins, or rivets as we now call them today, being 1¾in. The breaking load was stated to be 7 tons. When developing 18 bhp the chain tension was 25 cwts. It is said that some of the major items were supplied by Richard Garrett & Sons of Leiston, Suffolk, so probably the final erection took place in Ryburgh. This engine when completed was exhibited and tested at the Newcastle Upon Tyne RAS Show in 1887. Space will not permit the very extensive results to be given in full but the following important figures are most interesting:-

Efficiency of boiler	69.6%
ihp in HP cylinder	9.06
ihp in LP cylinder	12.05
Total	21.11
Indicated cut-off in HP	43.1%
Makers stated ihp	18

bhp after corrections for brake	16.93
Coal used per bhp per hour	3.746 lb
Mechanical efficiency $\frac{bhp}{ihp}$	80.1%
Working pressure	125 psi
Flywheel, diameter	4ft x 6½in wide
Heating surface. Tubes	98.3 sq ft
Firebox	23.0 sq ft
Smokebox	3.6 sq ft
Total	124.9 sq ft
Tubes, number x O/D	22 x 2½in

The value of these tests was that they showed the prospective buyer and user that the average traction engine, or portable for that matter, by a reputable maker was reasonably efficient and good value for money.

At the same time a single cylinder portable engine was being produced but unfortunately no illustration has become available.

However, I am able to show in Fig 196 one of the Company's single cylinder traction engines at work near Hethel, Norfolk, just before the end of the last century. It is unusual in as much that it has no tender, the manstand being a kind of glorified tailboard. There were two panniers, one either side of the tailboard, the right-hand for fuel and the left for water as will be seen in the photograph.

As we have noted in Figs 70 and 100 relating to Charles Burrell & Sons, the Universal Ploughing Engine was originated at Ryburgh, its design being based on Percival Everitt's Patent No 3553 sealed on 28th February 1879. The prototype was erected in the Ryburgh works after which Everitt, Adams & Co. entered into an Indenture Agreement with Charles Burrell & Sons dated 14th March 1881 to manufacture these engines for them and paying them a Royalty of 5% on the price of all engines sold. It is interesting to note that in this Indenture Agreement Percival Everitt and Thomas C. Cooper were nominated as executors of Percival Everitt and William John Adams. The first engine made by the Thetford firm was exhibited at the Kilburn Show in 1879. After some usual teething troubles had been eliminated, a second bearing Burrell's work's number 888 was shown at Carlisle in 1880.

Ryburgh Works then seemed to concentrate upon portables only, apart from much foundry and implement work, and their final design is illustrated in Fig 197. It is estimated about two dozens were made and today two are existing in private possession. The engine was a compound and the most interesting feature is that the cranks are set at 180° instead of the (continued on page 124)

PLAN

SECTION

END VIEW

122

Fig 195 (facing page) Farmer's Foundry Co and
P. Everitt's chain traction engine c1878.

Fig 197 A portable engine by the Farmer's Foundry Co.

Fig 196 One of Everitt's road engines at work in Norfolk.

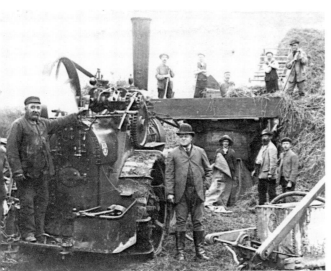

Fig 198 View inside the Great Ryburgh erecting shop.

usual 90°, an arrangement now only found in some makes of high speed enclosed forced lubrication engines. The cylinders are 5½in and 8in x 10in with the valve chests on the outside for accessibility. Flywheel 4ft 6in diameter x 8in face. The boiler contains 22 tubes x 2½in O/S diameter x 6 feet long and has double Salter safety valves. A Hartnell-Turner governor was fitted on the crankshaft. All details save the governors were made in the small works at Ryburgh of which in Fig 198 we have a delectable view of the erecting shop with a large compound cylinder block casting in the foreground.

This old firm went into liquidation in 1953 and is now under new proprietorship with the production of agricultural products still maintained.

✎ XVII ✎

JOHN GARROOD,
Wells Road, FAKENHAM.

In 1845 John Garrood had an Iron & Brass Foundry and was an Agricultural Implement Maker which he continued until after 1869, but by 1888 he had retired from business. In 1845 his was probably the only small jobbing foundry in that part of the county.

At one time he built a small portable with a single cylinder at the smokebox end and with the crank over the outer crown plate.

It is recorded that he made one or two small vertical engines but as with the portable, no further details appear to have been preserved.

✎ XVIII ✎

HAMBLING & SON,
Norwich Road, EAST DEREHAM.

Although long since defunct, this small firm was in business as early as 1836 when Thomas and Robert Hambling were described as Brassfounders in Norwich Road. By 1845 they had added Millwrights to their title and in 1854 Robert Hambling was classified as a "Whitesmith, Bell Hanger etc. and manufacturer of steam engines for agricultural purposes". Apparently the two brothers parted company as we find that Robert Hambling was in the Norwich Road and Thomas Hambling was in the High Street in 1864, after which no further mention is to be found of Thomas. In 1875 last mention was of Hambling & Son with the works in

Norwich Street (? Road) who were "Engineers, Millwrights and manufacturers of Prize Patent self-feeding Threshers". But two years later in 1877 the business had become acquired by Charles Middleton in Norwich Street.

During their later years they were responsible for several single cylinder portable engines, their details being typical at this period. Apart from that one was exhibited at the Royal Show at North Walsham in 1878 little authentic information is recorded about them or has come to light in recent times. Neither is it known how many were made, but two worked for many years in north central Norfolk.

It appears that at one time the firm carried out maintenance work on the tower windmill at the eastern boundary of the town and which has recently undergone some renovation.

✎ XIX ✎

HOLMES & SONS LTD.,
Prospect Place Works, NORWICH.

One of the leading Norwich agricultural and mechanical engineers established by John Holmes in Rising Sun Lane in 1827. In 1862 they greatly extended their premises and built the imposing glass and cast iron additional showroom still existing and fronting Castle Hill. At one time John Holmes exhibited no less than 112 types of small agricultural machinery at shows all over the country besides a variety of steam engines. It was perhaps this great variety of products that militated against economical production and caused the engine side to be gently phased out in the late 1890s, the factoring and supplying of ready-made oil engines taking their place. So it was in 1902 that the firm went into liquidation. At the later sale of the business the works came into the possession of Messrs. A. Pank & Son, heating and lighting engineers, whose headquarters were in Bedford Street, Norwich. They paid £1,640 for the front showroom, rear workshops and stores. Until 1907 F. R. Holmes continued in the lower works to produce a reduced range of implements previously manufactured, until his death in 1907. After that Messrs. Pank & Son acquired the whole of the site and buildings and therein repaired many engines of all types and makes. They still exist and repair work of one sort or another is still carried on.

John Holmes produced his first portable in 1855 and which series was made in from 4 to 12 nhp with single, and from 10 to 30 with duplex cylinders and a view of the single cylinder design is depicted in Fig 199. One was exhibited at the RAS Show at Worcester in 1863

HOLMES & SONS LIMITED NORWICH

Fig 199 Holmes of Norwich, their early portable and nameplate.

HOLMES & SONS ENGINEERS NORWICH

and won a medal. On test there, driving one of their threshing machines, it consumed only 462 lbs of best coal during a run of ten hours equivalent to 46.2 lbs per hour. The smallest of 6 nhp with a single cylinder cost £180 and the largest 25 nhp with duplex cylinders, £580.

In 1865 came their first traction engine illustrated in Fig 200, the three sizes of 6, 8 and 10 nhp the 6 & 8 having a single cylinder and the 10 nhp duplex cylinders. A differential cost £10 extra and winding

Fig 200 The first Holmes general purpose traction engine.

drum with 60 yards of wire rope £15 extra. In 1867 the 8 nhp single cylinder engine won a Silver Medal at the Fakenham Show. Its cylinder was 9in x 12in having the valve chest cast integral on the left-hand side, access to which was gained through the small cover so that port refacing was not too easy a matter. Note the long tie of massive cross-section bracing the front axle to the firebox front casing plate. A few of these early Holmes engines had a simple method for applying extra wheel-grip. The arrangement is seen in Fig 201 where all spokes were of double plates, having a set of four holes equally spaced. A wrought iron tongue shaped as shown

could be quickly pushed in or out as required, and the pin and its split-pin just as quickly refitted in the appropriate hole. A much quicker method than the fixing and taking off of spuds, especially with frozen fingers on a bitter cold day. Each rear wheel was driven by pins and thrust in by clutch bars worked from the footplate, thus eliminating the need for a man to get down to withdraw pins when rounding a sharp corner.

By the end of 1867 this design had been improved and modified into the robust machine depicted in Fig 202. In their specification the makers point out the boiler is of ample size and of great strength and are all *"tested to great pressure before leaving the works and fitted with Double Safety Valves and steam Pressure Indicator"*. They made the piston rod, slide bars and all motion gear of steel with the side brackets for crankshaft and intermediate shaft of wrought iron and all bearings were of gunmetal and adjustable. Two speeds were provided, giving 2 and 3 mph, and all gears were of cast steel. Engines of 10 nhp and upwards had a

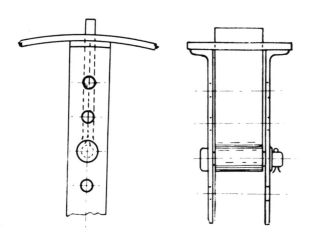

Fig 201 Holmes' method of increasing wheel grip.

Fig 202 The modified Holmes traction engine.

HOLMES AND SONS'
IMPROVED TRACTION ENGINES

AWARDED SILVER MEDAL AT FAKENHAM.

Fig 203 The last type of Holmes road engine and nameplate.

differential but the 6 and 8 nhp sizes "are made with easy means of throwing either wheel in or out of gear for turning sharp corners". However, for an extra charge compensating gear could be fitted to the smaller sizes also. List prices in the range were:-

6 nhp Cylinder 8in x 12in	£345
8 nhp Cylinder 9in x 12in	£400
10 nhp Cylinder 9½in x 12in and comp. gear	£480
12 nhp Duplex cylinders 2 x 8in x 12in	£580
Compensating gear to 6 and 8 nhp extra	£15
Winding drum and 60 yards of rope, extra	£15

In 1890, Prospect Place Works almost completely re-designed their road engine into the handsome machine included in Fig 203. It was now made only in 8 and 10 nhp sizes, the smaller having a cylinder 9in x 12in. The two brass lagging bands on the cylinder are very unusual but help the visual effect. Two speeds were provided; the hornplates had a long cutaway and the tall stovepipe chimney enhanced the silhouette. A good-looking engine whose proportions would bear comparison with many by some of the larger manufacturers. In 1890, these sizes cost £460 and £540 respectively. It is regretted that no example by this smaller maker is known to exist, but the nameplate is also shown in Fig 203.

Grasshopper engines were another type produced by John Holmes and his sons and at least two examples were installed in Eastern England. One at Chettisham, near Ely, was erected about 1870, together with a vertical spindle turbine pump to drain Layton's Level

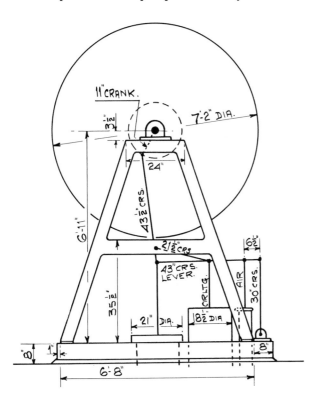

Fig 204 Diagram of a Holmes grasshopper engine in the Fens.

Fig 205 Photograph of the engine in Fig 204.

of 600 acres, the discharge being into the Great Ouse River. The single cylinder was 13½in x 22in and placed below ground, the upper end being supported by the cast iron bedplate which is shown in the diagram in Fig 204 and which also gives the main dimensions. In this form the connecting rod is attached to the end of the lever and combined with the piston rod. It will be seen that the two pumps, air and circulating, are also operated by the lever and towards its other end. A Meyer expansion valve was fitted on the back of the main slide valve. The crankshaft was extended through the wall and was supported on a third A frame in an annexe above the turbine pump well, the spindle being bevel driven. On the end of the crankshaft the driving

bevel wheel had 84 applewood teeth, and the driven cast iron bevel pinion had 28 teeth, providing a ratio of 3 : 1 up. A general view of the unit is included in Fig 205.

In Fig 206 we have another variation in grasshopper design where two equal cylinders were mounted below ground similarly to that in Fig 205 but both inside the two A frames. The crankshaft was again extended to a third A frame and carried the large driving bevel wheel having 110 teeth, the cast iron driven pinion on the top end of the turbine spindle having 42 teeth, giving a ratio of 2⅝ : 1 up. Both cylinders were 12in x 22in and the layout can be seen from the diagram in Fig 206. This interesting set was installed in Waxham, Norfolk, pumping station for drainage of about 700 acres, the view in Fig 207 showing clearly the two levers, each of two flitches. This form of grasshopper engine should be

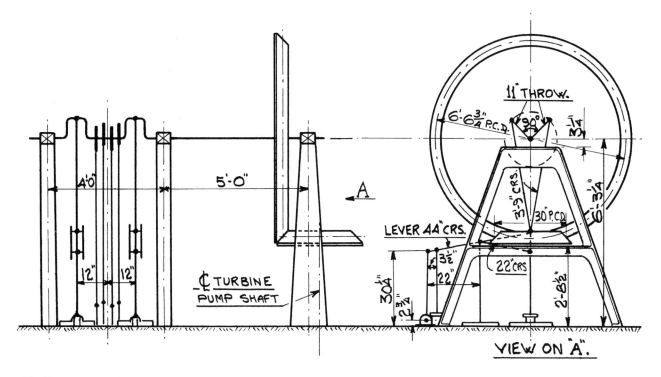

Fig 206 Diagram of a pair of Holmes grasshoppers formerly at Waxham.

Fig 207 Photograph of the Waxham grasshoppers by Holmes.

compared with that by Riches & Watts illustrated in Fig 244.

Besides these interesting grasshopper engines Holmes produced several horizontal engines with both single and double-crank compound cylinders and a reproduction of the single engine from an old engraving is to be seen in Fig 208. Their range was from 4 to 25 nhp but for powers upwards from 12 nhp the compound was advised. Holmes & Sons said of them, *"This engine is made throughout of the best materials*

Fig 208 Horizontal engine by Holmes of Norwich, with a single cylinder and nameplate.

and is carefully designed so as to give the greatest economy and regularity of working". Fig 208 also shows the appropriate nameplate.

When the double-crank compound engine was preferred it was as seen in Fig 209 with the condenser in tandem with and behind the low pressure cylinder, all mounted on a substantial cast iron bedplate. On trial one of these engines used 2½ lbs of coal per ihp per hour – an excellent figure. Another of this design was made and installed in c1878 to drain the Calthorpe Level near Acle, Norfolk. Originally the cylinders were 9½in and 15½in x 18in but subsequently the low pressure was bored to 15⅞in. On test by the writer in 1941 this engine indicated 56.2 ihp when turning over at 125 rpm and driving the vertical spindle turbine pump. A view on the cylinders is included in Fig 210. Sadly, this Norwich-built engine has been destroyed.

Naturally the homely vertical engine was available, if desired, and the Holmes example took the form shown in Fig 211 attached to its vertical boiler, both erected on a common cast iron bedplate. Both standards are gracefully curved, the upper and parallel portions being lined with slide bars for the crosshead. An eccentric driven feed pump completes the accessories. These were made in 2½, 3, 4, 6 and 8 nhp sizes listed at £70, £75, £90, £125 and £150 respectively.

Fig 210 A horizontal pumping engine from Prospect Place Works, Norwich.

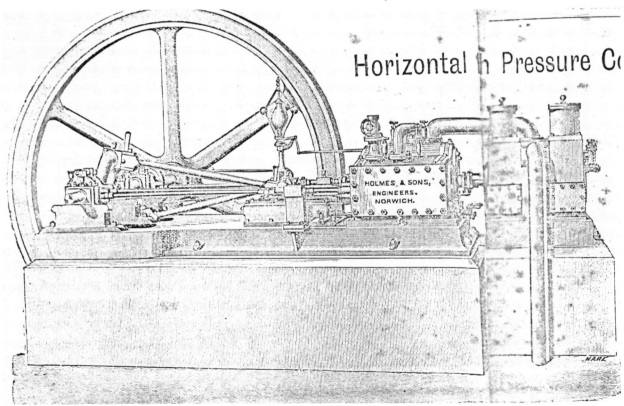

Fig 209 Engraving of a Holmes compound horizontal engine.

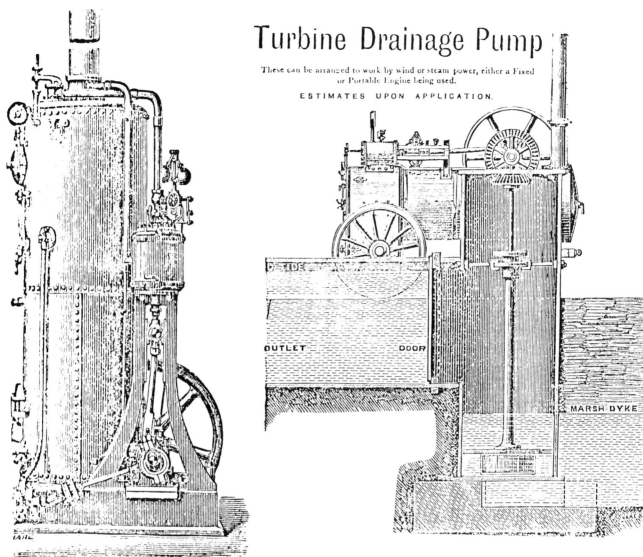

Turbine Drainage Pump

These can be arranged to work by wind or steam power, either a Fixed or Portable Engine being used.

ESTIMATES UPON APPLICATION.

Fig 211 The single cylinder vertical engine by Holmes & Son.

Fig 212 A Holmes portable geared to a vertical spindle Fen turbine pump.

Here I think it appropriate to show, in Fig 212, how a vertical spindle turbine pump was arranged. This illustration depicts a portable engine bevel geared to the pump spindle but in place of the portable a traction engine or other stationary vertical or horizontal engine could be used. The advantage of a self-moving or portable engine was that in dry sur..mer periods it could be taken away and used for other jobs instead of standing idle.

The impellor was the important part of the pump and a drawing of a typical Fen turbine impellor or fan is included in Fig 213. In working, water flows from the dyke and through the hole in the baseplate and is then centrifuged by the vanes thus causing the water to flow upwards until it finally floods through the discharge door and so into the main drain or river. One can easily demonstrate this principle by stirring half a cupful of

tea vigorously when it will overflow into the saucer. To make it continuous it would need a hole in the bottom of the cup to provide the feed!

Not many beam engines were made in Norfolk but one medium-sized example was made at the Prospect Place Works and then installed in Mendham Mill, Norfolk in 1871 where it worked until 1922. It was rather rare being a compound with cylinders 13½in and 32in, the stroke of the low pressure at the outer end of the beam being 45in. The piston rod of the high pressure was attached to the true point of the Watt parallel motion, whilst the low pressure was attached to the normal copied point, the linkage in this case being combined with the pantograph. Each cylinder had its slide valve worked by its own eccentric, the two eccentrics being placed side by side between the crankshaft bearing and the flywheel which was 13 feet in diameter. Normal speed was 42 rpm with steam at 45 psi and its rating was 25 nhp working condensing.

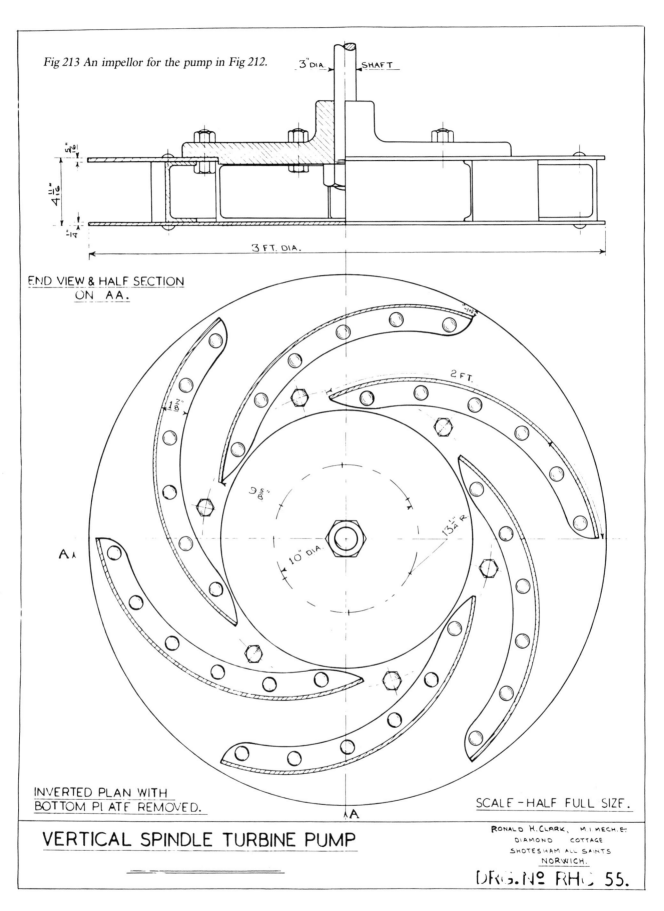

Fig 213 An impellor for the pump in Fig 212.

3" DIA. SHAFT

5/16"

4 11/16"

1/4"

3 FT. DIA.

END VIEW & HALF SECTION
ON AA.

1/2"

2 FT.

1 7/8"

9 5/8"

13 3/4" R

10" DIA.

A

INVERTED PLAN WITH
BOTTOM PLATE REMOVED.

A

SCALE – HALF FULL SIZE.

VERTICAL SPINDLE TURBINE PUMP

RONALD H. CLARK, M.I.MECH.E.
DIAMOND COTTAGE
SHOTESHAM ALL SAINTS
NORWICH.

DRG. No RHC 55.

XX

HENRY C. KEYMER,
Southtown Road, GREAT YARMOUTH.

Henry Keymer originally hailed from Norwich and after learning his trade there migrated to Yarmouth where, as early as 1879, he was established in a small works in the Southtown Road. But by 1883 he had moved to another small works in Gorleston.

He made several marine engines having duplex or compound cylinders. No illustration or other details appear to be available but it is recorded that one of his compounds was fitted in the small pleasure vessel *Lady of the Bure*. It was of straightforward design and typical of engines at that period.

XXI

DAVID H. KING,
Greenways Works, SUFFIELD.

One of only two present builders of steam engines now in the county, David King commenced manufacture at his small works in 1964 to supply a need for small engines suitable for commercial applications.

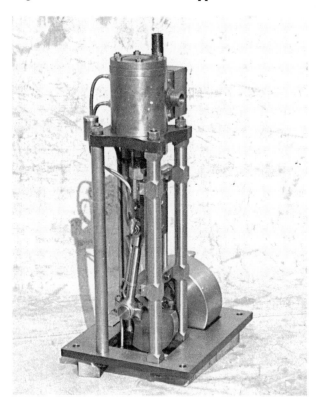

Fig 214 Single cylinder marine engine built by David H. King.

Norfolk being very much of a "water" county is home to many boats and hence his first engine was for a launch and is to be seen in Fig 214 having a single cylinder 2½in x 3in. Designed for a working pressure of 100 psi it produces 1½ shp, other outputs being proportional to the speed. Reversing is by the slip eccentric just visible behind the nearest column.

For larger vessels a compound engine is available, recorded in Fig 215, and this has cylinders 3in and 6in x 4in, being complete with boiler feed and air pumps for the condenser. Here again the output depends upon the speed appropriate to the vessel. Note the beautiful finish and that the columns are similar to those used in the single cylinder engine.

An entirely different type of engine is the Marshall general purpose traction engine illustrated in Fig 216, built to the scale of 5in to 1 foot, to special order. The single cylinder is 3½in x 5in and the finished engine is as near identical to the original Gainsborough product as it is possible to make it. A very fine engine indeed.

Another type of marine engine is depicted in the two views in Fig 217 showing the D. King stern paddle boat engine having duplex cylinders 3in x 18in giving the unusual bore stroke ratio of 1 : 6. A feed pump is driven from the crosshead having a bore of ⁵⁄₁₆in. This engine was installed in a boat named *Phoenix* which operates on the Birmingham-Worcester Canal. Probably the latest paddle boat engine to be made in the country.

Although many Uniflow engines were made elsewhere in the United Kingdom, especially in larger powers many of which exceeded 1,000 hp, King was the first maker to produce a uniflow engine in Norfolk and this was the exquisite example shown in Fig 218, made for a steam car. As will be noticed it is a vee four with both banks of cylinders at 90°, thus permitting starting in any crank position, the cylinders being 2¼in x 2½in single-acting using steam at 2,000 psi, and admitted through disc valves. As in most IC engines lubrication is dry sump. The Uniflow principle is simply that the exhaust is through a ring of ports at the end of the cylinder, these ports being uncovered by the piston just before the end of the stroke and they remain uncovered during the time the piston is stationary and the crankpin is moving through dead centre. In this way the inlet end of the cylinder is always at maximum temperature and the exhaust end at minimum temperature so that the heat drop is a maximum. There is therefore no heating and cooling of the admission end of the cylinder as with the ordinary contra-flow engine thus tending to greater efficiency and less steam consumption with little or no re-evaporation.

Fig 219 clearly shows the reversing mechanism utilising levers and chains to rotate the discshafts as required for reversing.

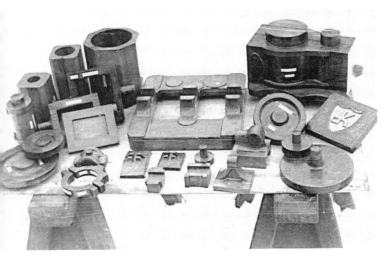

Fig 215 (above, right & below) David H. King's compound condensing marine engine.

Fig 216 Marshall-type single cylinder general purpose traction engine by D. H. King.

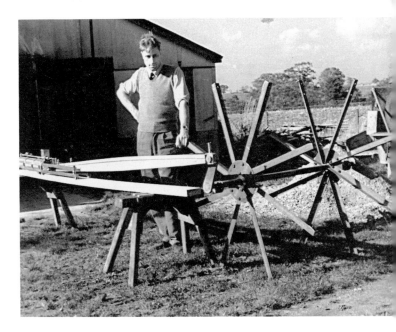

Fig 217 Two views of a stern wheel paddle engine from Suffield.

Fig 218 D. H. King's uniflow steam car engine.

Fig 219 Another view of the King uniflow car engine.

To steam engines using steam at high pressure demands a boiler quick to raise steam, small in dimensions and safe. Fig 220 illustrates King's boiler protected by Provisional Patent No 22075 of 1972. One will notice that it is of unusual configuration consisting as it does of a series of flat plates or fins held slightly apart by spacing washers, the whole set being clamped together as a unit by a tie-rod passing through the washers, centres of the fins and secured at each end by nuts threaded on the tie-rod. To ensure steam and pressure tightness at high pressures the assembly is usually brazed or welded together. Through each fin and near its centre in the cavity formed by the washers is a small communicating hole and this series of holes permits the working fluid to pass from end to end, i.e. from inlet as water to outlet as high pressure steam. The water is, of course, "flashed" into steam. With the fins made of copper, heat transference from the plates or fins to the water flowing through is very rapid. Another advantage is that with such a small amount of water in circulation, little damage can result from any disruption from this very small volume. What this novel form of boiler or heat exchanger looks like is to be seen from the photograph reproduced in Fig 220 and a boiler of this type is used for the Uniflow car engine referred to in Figs 218 & 219.

Fig 220 The King patent boiler and heat exchanger.

Fig 221 Locomotive Edmund Hannay from Suffield for 10¼in gauge.

Fig 222 Two views of a Pilgrim, a six-coupled King locomotive.

Few steam locomotives, apart from models, are in production today for serious work and it is therefore very refreshing to find passenger-hauling engines are in course of building in Suffield. An engine constructed in 1972 is shown in Fig 221. Named *Edmund Hannay*, it is of 10¼in gauge having cylinders 3½in x 5½in. The boiler is pressed to 100 psi, coal fired, and the feed is by injector but with an "Atthill" Scotch crank steam pump as an alternative. There is also a hand pump in case of dire necessity. Of the 0-4-2 wheel arrangement, it has outside frames.

A larger locomotive, built for the Wells & Walsingham Light Railway and completed in 1981, is illustrated in the two views in Fig 222 and in this case is a six-coupled tank engine, 0-6-0 type. Named *Pilgrim* it has cylinders 3¾in x 6in, the working pressure being 125 psi. The author was fortunate enough to witness the boiler lifted and mounted on the chassis in the maker's small erecting shop. It was first steamed on its railway on 28th April 1981.

All these types of engines built since 1965 are available for any customers as required and additionally, other or special engines can be constructed to meet any demand.

XXII

LAURENCE, SCOTT & CO. LTD., Gothic Works, NORWICH.

An extremely well-known firm established in 1883 by W. H. Scott and E. A. Paris, the firm's first title being Paris & Scott with premises at the Old Gothic Works, King Street, Norwich. In 1895 they moved to a new site at Thorpe, still called Gothic Works, and in 1896 R. E. Laurence joined the firm under the above title. By 1929 the Manchester concern of Electromotors Ltd., was acquired and the final title became Laurence, Scott & Electromotors Ltd. as they exist today.

Although W. H. Scott had many patents covering electrical technology to his credit, his patent relating to his own design of steam engine No 22349, accepted 16th November 1895, was very original and out-standing. We must remember that the second stage in a compound or two-stage expansion engine is usually obtained by transferring to a larger cylinder (the low pressure) the steam which has just completed the first stage of expansion in the smaller or high pressure cylinder. We can obtain the same result, however, by transferring only a portion of the steam which is already expanded in the first cylinder, in which case the second cylinder may be of the same size as the first and, of course, the amount of steam transferred will be further expanded in the second cylinder. What steam remains in the first or HP cylinder is retained for cushioning the piston, simultaneously being compressed up to the boiler pressure.

Instead of using two cylinders in the orthodox way Scott used one cylinder, the first stage of expansion taking place on top of the piston and the second stage on its bottom. So here we have yet another example of a single crank compound engine. This interesting steam cycle will be understood easily from a study of a set of indicator diagrams in Fig 223 taken by the writer when testing one of these engines in the power station at Gothic Works. After expanding from the point of cut-off as indicated, the steam then expands into the low pressure side underneath the piston, pushing it up and being cut off just after half stroke when it expands, and finally into the exhaust. The exhaust can be to a condenser, to process plant as in food production, or as in the case of the engine tested, into pipes for shop heating.

In Fig 224 are shown two sectional views to illustrate the construction of this engine and it will be noted that the piston is an annulus or ring connected to the crosshead by two piston rods. Working in the centre tunnel or liner is a piston valve having a number of ports in its circumference. Steam entering through the stop valve passes up between the inner and outer cylinder walls and covers and is admitted into the valve liner by ports A in the top. From the inside of the liner

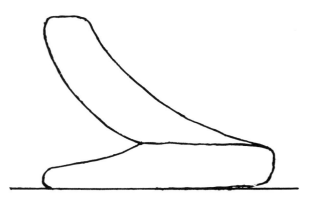

Fig 223 Indicator diagrams from W. H. Scott's Patent Engine.

the steam passes into the cylinder through the spiral ports C up the point of cut-off, the clearance space shown above the piston being already filled with steam up to initial pressure as we have seen from the indicator diagram; the cut-off being effected by the valve D, driven by the slide rod of the valve gear. After an early cut-off, the exact point of which is controlled by the governor, the steam expands, and when the crank is moving round bottom dead centre, the ports E in the centre of the liner and about half way in the stroke of

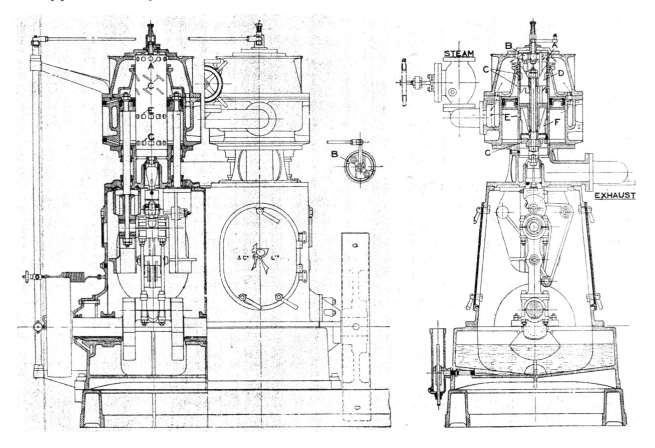

Fig 224 Cylinder details of the Scott engine.

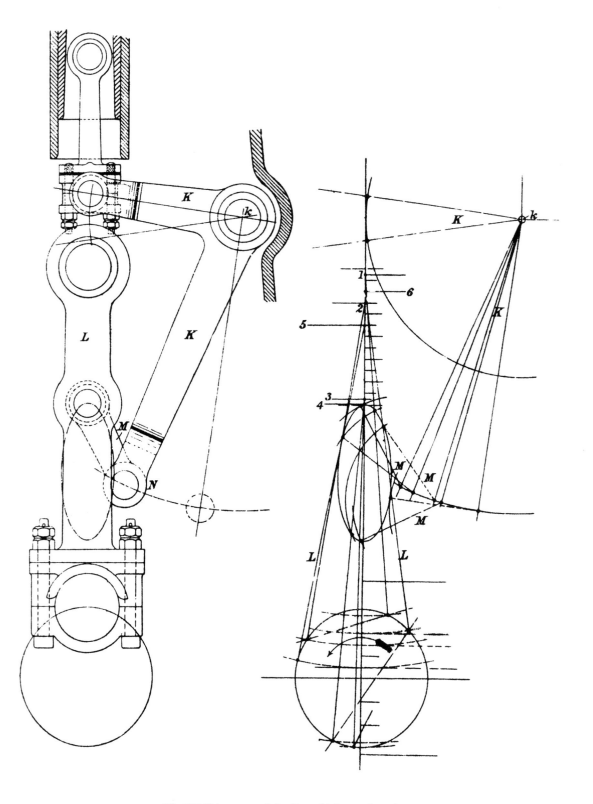

Fig 225 Valve gear of the Scott high speed engine.

the piston, are operated by the valve F designated by Scott as the transfer and exhaust valve.

The valve F at the same time opens the ports G at the bottom of the cylinder so that while the piston is making its up-stroke a communication is made between the top and bottom of the cylinder transferring steam at equal pressure and temperature from the top to the bottom of the annular piston and this transference continues for about half stroke. So in effect therefore we have half of the steam once above the piston now operating on the other or underside. This important transference is closed first by the piston over-running the ports E during its up-stroke and immediately afterwards by the valve F closing the ports E & G. The steam now on the underside of the piston completes its expansion and at the end of the up-stroke the exhaust valve opens and the steam exhausts.

The steam which had remained above the piston is compressed and clearances are such that at the end of the stroke this pressure equals that of the incoming steam. This compression ensures adequate cushioning as seen from the indicator diagram and moreover, also ensures that the heat of compression raises the temperature up to that of the incoming steam. I think it obvious therefore that by this simple means there is no cooling of the incoming steam, therefore no loss in pressure and no condensate. In other words the thermal efficiency is high.

Very accurate speed control is secured by a crank-shaft governor working through levers on the governor bridge B and controls the point of cut-off by the valve D. This valve D though reciprocated by the valve gear with a constant stroke is free to be rotated by the guide studs on the bridge B and the ports in this admission valve D are so arranged in connection with the ports in the valve liner itself that a slight axial movement will naturally cause an alteration in the cut-off. To put it succinctly, we have yet another form of automatic expansion regulator.

Another very interesting part in the design is the valve operation, in this case another variant of radial valve gear. Like other radial valve gears it can trace its ancestry back to the original gear of John Wesley

Fig 226 Side prospect of a two-crank Scott-Reavell engine.

Hackworth, covered by his Patent No 2448 and sealed on 26th October 1859. In the Scott gear shown in the diagram in Fig 225 L is the connecting rod, K a bell-crank lever pivoted at a fixed point X in the frame of the engine and M a short connecting link between the connecting rod and the long end N of the bell-crank lever. The upper arm of the lever K is pin-joined at P to the lower end of the valve rod R attached by an ordinary gudgeon pin to the piston valve S. Its action should now be clear from a study of the diagram.

What the complete engine looks like is shown in the photograph reproduced in Fig 226, showing the two-crank engine in the private power station formerly in Gothic Works. It is shown coupled direct to one of the firm's large dc generators. The other engine in this power station was a single cylinder engine similarly coupled to, of course, a smaller dynamo.

On test a 100 kW two-crank set working condensing returned the excellent results seen in the following table:—

No. of Test	Steam Pressure psi	Vacuum in Inches	rpm	Amps	Volts	kW	ihp	Steam in lbs per ihp per hour	kW per hour	Combined Efficiency %	Remarks
I	149	25¼	444	248.6	506	125.8	203.7	15.9	25.75	82.6	Overload test
II	150	25½	446	199.0	500.4	100.2	159.5	15.48	24.7	84.0	Full load test
III	149	25½	448	149.0	505.5	75.3	125.0	15.6	25.94	80.75	¾ – load test
IV	151	26	453	100.0	500.0	50.0	88.1	15.65	27.6	76.0	½ – load test

It was found, however, that manufacture of these steam engines alongside direct current machinery caused various difficulties, and so Scott, aided by his brother-in-law William Reavell, started a new works in Ranelagh Road, Ipswich in 1898 for the sole manufacture of the Scott Patent Engine. Later, it was designated the Scott-Reavell Engine. By 1904, one, two and three crank engines had been supplied to power stations in many localities including Horsham, Dartford, Heckmondwike, Barnstaple, South Africa and – Ipswich!

Single cylinder engines were available in six sizes, the cylinder varying from 12 in x 6in to 17in x 8 in. Two-crank engines varied from 12 in x 6in to 24in x 14in covering nine powers or sizes, and the three-crank varied from 14in x 7in to 24in x 14in, there being seven sizes in this range.

All these engines ran silently, smoothly and without any apparent vibration as the writer can testify from personal experience.

Unfortunately not one appears to have been preserved in any locality.

✆ XXIII ✆
EDWIN LEFEVRE,
Stamp Office Yard, NORWICH.

This was a small engineering business first commenced by Thomas Lefevre in St. Stephen's Street and by 1858 was well established. In 1865 he had moved to premises at the junction of Rose Lane with Prince of Wales Road. Then by 1883 the title was Edwin Lefevre, who had moved the works to St. Andrew's Broad Street, finally finishing up in Stamp Office Yard in 1896. After this date the late William Lefevre told me his father closed the business, the plant and premises being sold.

Several types of engine were made – horizontals, verticals, entablature and marine. The commonest size had a cylinder 8in x 10in. One of the entablatures – a type where the cylinder is fitted on the bedplate and driving up to the crankshaft carried in bearings mounted on the square entablature supported on four corner columns – drove a pump for many years at the Abbey Farm, Langley, Norfolk. Here again further details are lacking. Lefevre did remark to me, however, that at one time the firm's notepaper bore a small line illustration of one of their entablature engines.

A small marine engine said to have been a "diagonal" with duplex cylinders 5in x 7in was made and fitted in a launch named *Despatch*, built in 1880, which was 41 feet long. Apparently it was built by J. Teasdale of Stalham, Norfolk, but further details

have not been found. Although described as a "diagonal", quite probably it was of the vee twin formation.

✆ XXIV ✆
THOMAS LEPARD,
Cobholm, GREAT YARMOUTH.

Thomas Lepard had premises in the Yarmouth suburb of Cobholm which, when he closed down in 1916, were then acquired by A. Webber & Sons (see No XLI). He was responsible for several compound surface condensing marine engines, two of which were fitted in the steam drifters *Lord Bobs* and *Queen Alexandra* and another in the river passenger boat *Cobholm*. They were of typical straightforward design, those in *Lord Bobs* and *Cobholm* having cylinders 10in and 20in x 12in and that in *Queen Alexandra* 11in and 22in x 14in. Unfortunately no photograph or other illustration has turned up.

Besides engines of these dimensions a number of much smaller examples of about 4 hp were made having both compound and duplex cylinders.

The most interesting of all was his "Vertical-Horizontal" compound where the high pressure cylinder was vertical and the low pressure horizontal, both big ends working on the common crankpin. Several were used for small craft and land purposes but again concise details are now unknown. Such engines, however, in very large sizes, were made by some north country firms for rolling-mill drives.

✆ XXV ✆
H. A. O. MACKENZIE, SCOLE.

Mr Mackenzie anticipated by twenty eight years S. G. Soames's idea of a steam passenger vehicle (See No XXXV) in his steam Brougham which first appeared on Norfolk roads in 1874 and this is illustrated in Fig 227.

The power was developed in two cylinders each 3¾in x 4½in and was transmitted to the countershaft by gearing and finally to the back axle by pitch chain. Two speeds were incorporated in the gearing, giving ratios of 6 and 13 : 1. Two driving wheels four feet in diameter carried the rear while the single front steerage wheel was tiller operated by the driver from inside the vehicle.

Fig 227 The Steam Brougham by H.A.O. Mackenzie
of Scole.

Steam was supplied from a Field-type vertical boiler pressed to 135 psi and the normal speed was 10/12 mph with its full complement of four passengers. It ran quietly and smoothly for many hundreds of miles on roads in South Norfolk and it was said to have been a real all-weather machine and easily handled.

What ultimately became of it I have not been able to discover.

MIDLAND & GREAT NORTHERN JOINT RAILWAY,
Locomotive Works, MELTON CONSTABLE.

This railway, probably the largest "Joint" railway in the United Kingdom, was formed from a number of smaller railways in Lincolnshire and Norfolk. Briefly, these smaller lines were the Norwich & Spalding, Spalding & Bourne, the Peterborough & Sutton Bridge, the Yarmouth & North Norfolk and the Lynn & Fakenham. Those lines to the East of Lynn became upon amalgamation in 1883 the Eastern & Midlands, and those west of Lynn became the Midlands & Eastern. These two major systems were formed into the M&GNJ on 1st July 1893.

As the link-up of the Yarmouth & N. Norfolk with the Lynn & Fakenham was formally achieved, the site for a central repair works had been chosen at Melton Constable and by 1880 the ground had been prepared and buildings were being erected. Additionally, the Norwich-Spalding line joined in from Norwich at Melton Constable. In this way the village became both the locomotive and the railway centre.

At the commencement all the activity in Melton shops was devoted to repairs and maintenance of all classes of rolling stock. The first major locomotive work

Fig 228 Cornish Minerals Railway tank locomotive sold to the Lynn & Fakenham Railway.

was, strictly speaking, not the making of a new engine, but sufficiently important to deserve recording in this book. In 1874 Sharp, Stewart & Co. had built for the ill-fated Cornish Minerals Railway eighteen six-coupled tank engines with weatherboards in place of cabs, as seen in Fig 228, the intention being to operate them in pairs working back to back. Later Sharp, Stewart took them back and three were then sold to the Lynn & Fakenham Railway in December 1880. In March 1881 another five were acquired by this railway who had thus increased their stock of locomotives by eight very useful and practically new engines. Their main dimensions were as follow:–

Cylinders	16¼in x 20in
Wheels, coupled, diameter	3ft 6in, later 3ft 7½in
Wheelbase, leading to driving	5ft 0in
Wheelbase, driving to trailing	6ft 0in
Wheelbase total	11ft 0in
Boiler barrel, mean diameter	4ft 0⅜in
Boiler barrel, length	8ft 2in
Firebox, width	4ft 0in
Firebox, length	3ft 11in
Firebox, height	5ft 2in
Tubes	195 x 1¾in O/D
Heating surface, firebox	70.7 sq ft
Heating surface, tubes	752.8 sq ft
Heating surface, total	823.5 sq ft
Grate area	10.82 sq ft
Working pressure	140 psi
Tank capacity	780 gallons
Fuel capacity	15 cwt
Weight in working order on leading wheels	10 ton 7 cwt
Weight in working order on driving wheels	10 ton 17 cwt
Weight in working order on trailing wheels	9 ton 12 cwt
Weight in total	30 ton 16 cwt
Weight empty	24 ton 10 cwt
Fuel consumption on passenger work	28 lb per mile
Load on goods work, i.e. 30 sheeted wagons, max	300 ton
Tractive Effort @ 80% boiler pressure	14,083 lb
Height to top of chimney	12ft 6in
Height to centre-line of boiler	6ft 1in
Height to centre-line of buffers	3ft 3in
Height to top of running plate	3ft 9½in
Centres of buffers	5ft 9in
Overall length	30ft 5⅞in
Overall width	8ft 6in

Some had a small four-wheeled tender fitted and which was supplied by the makers.

On the long stretches between stations in West Norfolk, but solely because of their having driving wheels only 3ft 6in diameter, it was hard work keeping to time with passenger trains and therefore the company's Chief Engineer, the late William Marriott, decided on a metamorphosis at Melton Works in 1890. No 18 was the first to be altered and Marriott substituted 4ft 7in diameter driving wheels at the rear, leaving the original leading wheels, of course un-coupled, at 3ft 6in diameter. Altering driving wheel sizes leads to other fundamental alterations which will be appreciated from a study of the original drawing by Sharp Stewart, reproduced in Fig 229. It became necessary therefore to raise the whole locomotive 2½in to accommodate this new diameter. The horn spaces were cut away at the top allowing the axleboxes to rise, the frame being strengthened by cover plates fitted inside. New horn cheeks had to be fitted for each of the six axleboxes as they had to work lower in the horn spaces. Similarly, the cylinders, slide bars, and motion had to be altered to fit the new driving centres. At the same time new drain cocks were fitted. Naturally, new cast steel driving wheels were called for and the leading axleboxes were given more side-play by having sliding tops. Side tanks were dispensed with but new cabs were provided together with splashers and sandboxes com-bined. Other fittings comprised Holt & Gresham steam sanding gear and sight-feed lubricators in the cab in place of the old bulb lubricators on the smokebox. After this extensive rebuilding the main dimensions became:–

Cylinders	16in x 20in
Wheelbases	as before
Driving wheels, diameter	4ft 7in
Bogie wheels, diameter	3ft 6in
Tender capacity, water	876 gall
Tender capacity, coal	45 cwt
Loads	as before

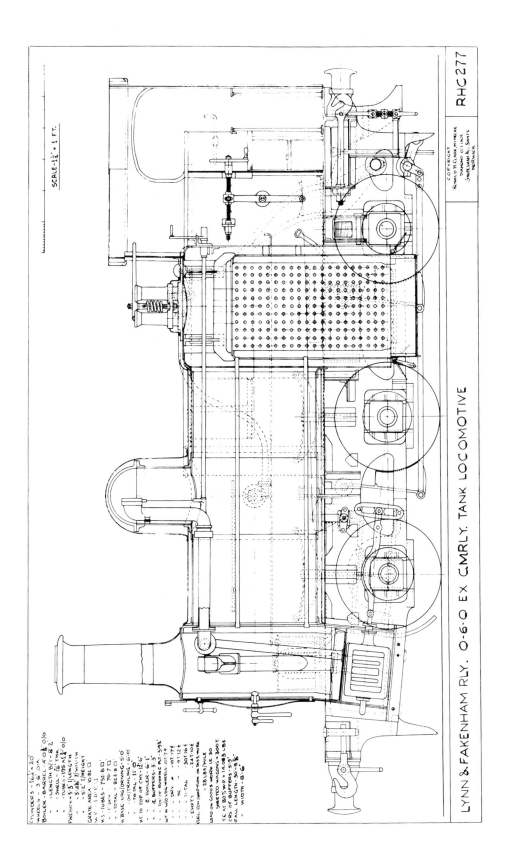

LYNN & FAKENHAM RLY. 0·6·0 EX C.M.RLY. TANK LOCOMOTIVE

SCALE-1½ = 1 FT.

RHC 277

COPYRIGHT
RONALD H CLARK, MITBEME
DIAMOND COTTAGE
SWITCHAM AL, SANTS
NORWICH.

Fig 229 General arrangement of the engine in Fig 228.

What these practically new engines looked like is apparent from the view of No 18 depicted in Fig 230, coupled up with its tender supplied by Sharp, Stewart. We have therefore a very serviceable 2-4-0 tender locomotive now suitable for local passenger working and through goods trains. Altogether four were thus converted and in the E&M List they were numbered 3, 13, 14 and 18. The four not rebuilt, Nos 1, 2, 11 and 12 were withdrawn in 1899, 1898, 1899 and 1902 respectively.

The remaining four engines of the original class were later "rebuilt" into the picturesque machine seen in Fig 231. But in actual fact they were virtually new engines as not much of the originals was found serviceable. Melton shops at the same period produced five more of this class. One some the original wheels had ten spokes of rectangular cross-section, and others twelve spokes of elliptical cross-section, obviously new wheels bought out from Sharp, Stewart. Engines with ten spoke wheels had the left-hand crank leading and the twelve spoke wheels had the right-hand crank to lead. The makers had fitted Allen straight link motion but Melton Constable altered all to Howes motion. These nine new and very useful mixed traffic engines as we may call them were re-numbered 14A (Oct 1897), 1A (Aug 1899) 11A (Aug 1899), 3A (Dec 1899), 15 (1900), 17A (March 1902), 12A (Dec 1902), 2A (Jan 1903), and 16 (May 1905). Nos 15 and 16 retained the suffix A until scrapped, but the remaining seven were then numbered 93–99 until scrapping took place. The last to go was No 16, scrapped in August 1949 and it was working almost until that date. An excellent testimony to the Melton craftsmen.

A third class of locomotive was designed and made at Melton comprising three 4-4-2 Tank engines of handsome appearance as may be seen from the photograph reproduced in Fig 232. Again, for accountancy purposes, they were classed as rebuilds. At this juncture let me confess I am not at all clear as to what was then meant by "accountancy purposes"!

These engines, numbered by the Joint, were 41, built Dec 1904, 20, built Feb 1909 and 9, built March 1910. Their main dimensions were as follow:-

Cylinders	18¼in x 24in
Driving wheels	6ft 0in diameter
Trailing wheels	3ft 6½in diameter
Wheelbase, bogie	6ft 6in
Wheelbase bogie to front driving	10ft 3in
Wheelbase, coupled	8ft 6in
Wheelbase, rear driving to trailing	7ft 6in

Wheelbase total	29ft 6in
Weight, on bogies	19 ton 15 cwt
Weight, on front driving	17 ton 18 cwt
Weight, on rear driving	17 ton 12 cwt
Weight on trailing driving	13 ton 4 cwt
Weight total	68 ton 9 cwt
Boiler, barrel	4ft 2in diameter
Boiler, length between tubeplates	10ft 10⅝in
Boiler, firebox, length outside	5ft 11in
Boiler, firebox, width outside	4ft 1in
Boiler, firebox, height inside	5ft 5in to 6ft 0in
Boiler tubes	196 x 1¾in O/D
Heating surface, tubes	989 sq ft
Heating surface, firebox	110 sq ft
Heating surface, total	1,099 sq ft
Grate area	17½ sq ft
Working pressure	160 psi
Tanks, capacity	1,650 gall
Coal, capacity	2 ton
Rail to centreline of buffers	3ft 5in
Rail to centreline of boiler	7ft 6in
Rail to top of chimney	12ft 11⁹⁄₁₆in

Fig 230 The rebuild of the Sharp, Stewart engine to a 2-4-0.

Length over buffers	38ft 8in		Tractive effort @	
Width over footplate	8ft 6in		80% working pressure	12,696 lb
Width over cab, outside	8ft 0in		Adhesive factor	6.26

Fig 231 Another rebuild to a 0-6-0 tank engine.

Fig 232 A Melton Constable-built 4-4-2 express tank locomotive.

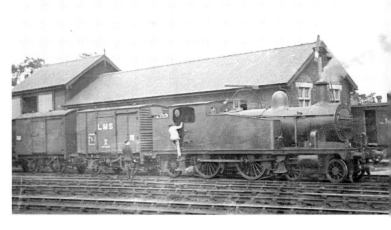

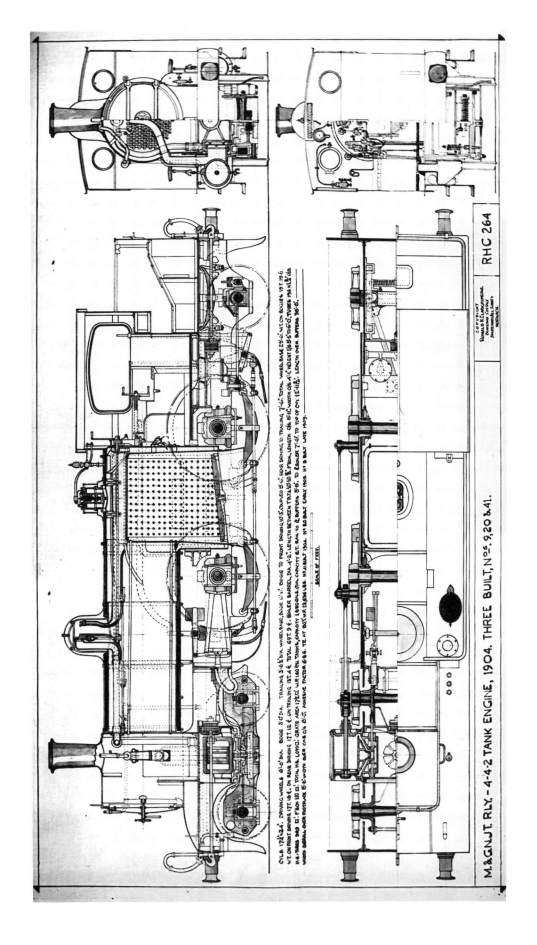

Fig 233 General arrangement drawing of the 4-4-2 Melton engines.

148

The boilers were of Midland Railway origin, their Class B, and of Deeley pattern with closed dome, and they were the only engines on this railway to use this class of boiler. Inevitably there were slight differences. For example, No 41 had a short smokebox, the standard Joint number plates and spokes of rectangular cross-section in the coupled wheels. Nos 20 and 9 had extended smokeboxes and their numbers formed of cut-out brass figures. During a conversation my late father H. O. Clark had with Mr. Marriott on one occasion, my father understood that the sets of motion gear, cylinders and driving wheels were bought out from Beyer, Peacock & Co. Ltd., who had supplied some years previously fifteen 4-4-0 tender express locomotives with cylinders 17in x 24in, of which the parts just mentioned were interchangeable. It was obviously the logical and practical thing to do. The extra quarter inch in the cylinder bores were easily provided as the original patterns were for bores from 17in to 17½in. In Fig 233 we see a general arrangement drawing for these three engines which may prove helpful to the prospective model maker. They would certainly make an attractive and unusual subject for a model at, say, 5in gauge. Withdrawal dates of these three locomotives were No 20, April 1942, No 41, January and No 9, in July, 1944. Although all the design and manufacture, apart from the boilers, was carried out at Melton, it appears the drawing office borrowed drawings of the trailing wheels and axle from the LT&S Railway whose famous tank engines on the Fenchurch-Southend

surburban service must be known to many readers.

A fitting conclusion to this record of the Melton Works that are alas no more, is to recapture the great erecting shop in the zenith of its activity, as depicted in Fig 234, where no less than ten engines are in divers stages of re-erection or repair. At one time the overhead travelling crane was steam-operated as the writer remembers very clearly. More details are visible in Fig 235 and showing up largely in the foreground is one

Fig 234 The main erecting shop at Melton Constable.

Fig 235 Further interesting details in the Melton erecting shop.

of the 4-4-2 tank engines under construction, those 196 tubes being unmistakeable. To the left is No 96 undergoing heavy repairs and with the side tanks and cab lying nearby ready for re-fitting after the boiler has been mounted. Melton shops, like those in St. Nicholas Works, Thetford, provided first-class training for any apprentice. In fact the sort of works where the writer could willingly have spent two years or more!

⤙ XXVII ⤚

NICHOLAS PARKER, BARNEY.

The first mention of this small village engineer was in 1869 when he described himself as a Blacksmith. In 1888 he was also an Agricultural Implement Maker but no account of him is to be found in 1900.

He built a small portable engine towards the end of last century, the crank being overhung and with the feed pump at the side, and part of, the single cylinder, as will be seen from the photograph reproduced in Fig 236. The flywheel, if not from a chaff-cutter, was certainly identical to those he fitted to his own make of implement, and the same applies to the road wheels.

The boiler feed system is very ingenious and also forms a good example of natural East Anglian rural inventiveness. Alongside the boiler, and clearly seen in the picture, is a feed pipe inside a larger exhaust pipe, the annular space between them being filled with steam to form an admirable feed water heater. This exhaust steam finally travels to the chimney base as will be seen. The pipe coming up from behind the front wheel is, of course, the feed. Above the pump is a two-way valve by

Fig 236 The unique village portable engine by Nicholas Parker.

means of which water not being delivered into the boiler is by-passed to the tank just visible. Note the pump is driven off the crosshead. On the offside is the slide valve and a Salter safety valve. With such a long boiler the heating surface must have been ample for a cylinder 6½in x 10in. With the chimney hinge and crutch at about the same level, the chimney, when lowered, would be practically horizontal, the idea being that therefore it formed a better "ridge" to support the tilt.

For many years this odd and curious little engine was owned and used by the late J. Attwill Palmer of Southacre. It is believed it finished its working life in Briston.

valves to the intermediate and low pressure cylinders, the working pressure being 180 psi. The actual ihp on trial was 273.7, the boilers being standard marine drybacks 10 feet in diameter x 9ft 6in long.

The first engine was built in 1920 and fitted to the steam drifter *Byng*, the second being completed in 1922 and also fitted in a drifter, named *Lord Anson*, in 1927. Both boats were registered at Lowestoft and later worked as drifter-trawlers.

It is unfortunate that as yet no illustration of one of these engines by this smaller maker has come to light.

XXVIII

HENRY PEACOCK, BINHAM.

Henry Peacock had as early as 1845 established a small village foundry and was described as Founder and Machine Maker in 1858 and 1869. He was still in business in 1888 after which and by 1900 the goodwill was continued by Thomas Lake.

It would be in c1890 that he produced a small and rudimentary single cylinder portable engine of about 2 nhp. The flywheel was off a large chaff-cutter and the engine was built to power a horse-powered thresher. The road wheels and flywheel are said to have been similar to those on some of his agricultural implements, but unfortunately little more is known of this "one-off" village effort.

XXX

J. POWELL,
High Road, BRANCASTER.

The founder of this small business, Charles Powell, was born in 1850 and when only twenty years of age made a small horizontal engine with an automatic expansion regulator. As a young man he started on his own account with a small foundry and smithy and by 1890 had taken into partnership his son Joseph, to make it Powell and Son as it existed for some years after World War 2.

This small engine made by Charles Powell is illustrated in Fig 237 having a cylinder 1⅝in x 2½in. The governor raises or lowers the expansion link thus altering the stroke of the side valve, that is the cut-off, to suit the load. It was his intention to build larger examples for industry but at that time other work intervened. This engine is now treasured in the writer's possession.

Fig 237 Charles Powell's small experimental horizontal engine.

XXIX

PERTWEE & BACK LTD.,
Nelson Ironworks, GREAT YARMOUTH.

Established originally by Samuel V. Moore "Anchor Smith" c1810, who, among several types, made an interesting beam engine with a single cylinder. The business continued in the Moore family until c1899 when the late H. A. Pertwee became an interested partner, being joined by the late W. H. Back in 1900 when it was registered as Pertwee & Back Ltd. It flourishes as such today, but is engaged more in the motor car trade.

In later years, after 1900, Pertwee & Back Ltd. have designed and produced two large triple expansion marine engines having cylinders 9½in and 16in and 26in x 18in with piston valves to the high, and slide

It was during the period 1875 to 1880 that three larger engines were made. The first two were semi-portables or overtypes of 5 nhp with a single cylinder using steam at 80 psi. They were sold to a chemical works in Yorkshire.

The third was an ordinary portable engine, also of 5 nhp and at the same time a threshing machine was made to go with it. Later, the engine was brought back and used to drive the works. Save boiler fittings, all parts and boilers were made at Brancaster, no mean feat in such a small works, as Joseph Powell mentioned to me.

Again it is unfortunate that no illustrations of these later engines have come to light.

Fig 238 Riches & Watts single cylinder portable engine.

⬥ XXXI ⬥

RICHES & WATTS,
Duke's Palace Ironworks, NORWICH.

James Watts originally established his small foundry c1829/30 in Rose Lane, Norwich and produced a run of miscellaneous iron castings. In 1845 his title was James Watts & Co. and as it prospered he joined with two partners, Howard and Riches, to form Howard, Riches & Watts. With a new foundry located close to the old Duke's Palace in 1858, this site was named the Duke's Palace Ironworks. Their offices were in Golden Ball Street for some years. However, after thirty years or so Howard and Watts had deceased, causing the old firm to be styled Riches & Co. early in 1890. By 1900 the concern had closed and today every trace of both the Duke's Palace and the Ironworks are erased and the sites covered by unprepossessing car parks and telephone buildings.

At one period portable engines formed the "bread and butter" of their trade to the agricultural community and they were available in two types, the single cylinder and the tandem compound. The single cylinder is illustrated in Fig 238 with a large boiler, square chimney base and wooden wheels, rated at 8 nhp, the range covering 2½ to 12 nhp sizes. Above this rating and up to 20 nhp duplex cylinders were used. All boilers were of best Staffordshire iron, fire boxes of Lowmoor and tested hydraulically to 100 psi. They gave many years of service and the writer saw one at work as late as 1941.

In Fig 239 is shown the tandem compound engine having the HP cylinder cantilevered behind the LP, with its slide valve on the right-hand side and that for the LP on the left-hand side. Here the wheels are of iron and the complete engine was more than a ton lighter than the heavier type seen in Fig 238. The makers said

Fig 239 A rare tandem compound by Riches & Watts.

Fig 240 A semi-portable or overtype from Duke's Palace Ironworks.

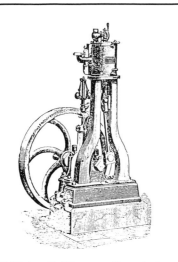

Fig 241 Riches & Watts small vertical engine.

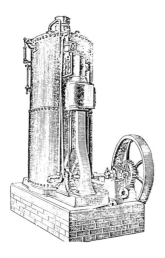

Fig 242 Another rare engine – the tandem compound vertical by Riches & Watts.

Fig 243 Riches & Watts double crank compound vertical engine.

this light tandem compound "*is perfect master of a full size Finishing Threshing Machine*".

It is not a big step from a portable to a semi-portable or over-type as has been mentioned earlier and the Riches & Watts example is depicted in Fig 240. Very similar to the single cylinder portable, it had a neat front pedestal and strong cast iron ashpan doubling as the rear support.

Having made patterns for the HP cylinder of the tandem compound portable, it was an obvious step to use this cylinder for their smaller sizes of high speed vertical, one of which is illustrated in Fig 241. Note the engine and vertical boiler are combined on a common bedplate and any part of the unit is very accessible. They were marketed in ten sizes, viz. 1½, 2, 2½, 3, 4, 5, 6, 8, 10 and 12 nhp but above 4 nhp a cylinder designed for this particular range was used. The 1½ nhp cost £50, the 2½, £72, the 8, £160 and the 12 nhp was priced at £220. A standard boiler had cross tubes but vertical tubes could be supplied, if desired. As *Engineering* put it, "*A very neatly designed Combined Vertical Engine and Boiler*". If a boiler was not ordered by the customer, the governor was mounted on a cast iron pedestal between the eccentric and the outer flywheel bearing. *Engineering's* comment, incidentally, referred to the engine exhibited at the RAS Show at Oxford.

Another variation was to put the tandem compound portable block on a pair of standards and on a common bedplate with the boiler, as can be seen in Fig 242 which shows very clearly the two eccentrics, one on either side of the cylinders. The larger capacity feed pump was spur gear driven near the flywheel. Their range was limited to five powers, viz. 4, 6, 8, 10 and 12 nhp, the first costing £180 and the largest £285. Riches & Watts said of them, "*The most economical engine of the day*". Fig 242 illustrates the 6 nhp engine having cylinders 4½in and 7in x 10in using steam at 80 psi and running at 180 rpm, developing 12½ ihp. The boiler was 2ft 10in diameter x 6ft 8in high. The boiler used 3½ lb of best coal per indicated horsepower per hour. The feed pump was worked by an eccentric cast on the same cogwheel which also operated the air pump and feed from the hotwell on top of the condenser. The air pump was single-acting and placed inside the condenser. It worked by the gearing as seen at 1 : 1½ of engine speed. These engines could be converted into non-condensing by disengaging the exhaust pipe and fixing another pipe that led from the exhaust into the chimney.

When a much more powerful engine was called for, the customer could have a nicely-proportioned vertical two-crank compound depicted in Fig 243. They all had steam-jacketed cylinders cast from a special mixture of iron. There was a condenser at the rear of the engine and a force pump for the feed. The high speed governor had the links and pins totally enclosed and gave governing to within very fine limits of speed. They were available in 10 to 100 nhp and the manufacturers stated, "*The indicated or actual power of 2½ to 3 times the nominal power according to the steam pressure*". Several were made for local flour mills and factories.

In Fig 244 is shown the simple design of grasshopper engine made by the firm during the 1860s. It is probably the only engine of this type to be made in the county and is of plain straightforward design. The cylinder, about 10in x 24in, is lagged with polished strip mahogany, the ports of the "long" variety being cast in, the stroke of the slide valve being comparatively short. A large Watt-type governor, boiler feed pump and heavy flywheel complete the main details. The lever was of two plates or "flitches". It is informative to compare this arrangement of grasshopper engine where the connecting rod drives downwards and the alternative form we have noticed as made by Holmes & Sons (No XIX). The Grasshopper Straight Line Motion, used in this case to guide the crosshead in a straight line, was so-called due to its action in motion resembling that of a grasshopper when rubbing its body with its legs, thus causing the peculiar noise associated with it.

Those customers preferring a horizontal engine had a choice of powers from 4 to 20 nhp where the single cylinder was cantilevered over the end of the bedplate. One of 20 nhp with a 10in bore cylinder was made in 1872 for Norwich Gasworks. If desired, a compound horizontal was available, the commonest size having

cylinders 10in and 18in x 14in, rated at 60 nhp. One of this type worked for many years in Pockthorpe Brewery, Norwich. Installed in 1879, it was still in sound order when the brewery closed down shortly after 1960.

Perhaps one of the best horizontal engines made at Duke's Palace Ironworks was completed in 1887 and installed by the firm in Langley Upper Pumping Station, Norfolk, that year to drive a large turbine pump, also of their manufacture. One particularly interesting point is that this engine was not designed by Riches & Watts but by Edward Easton, a partner in that world-famous concern Easton, Amos & Anderson, whose works were at Erith, Kent and who over a long period made many pumping engines of various types for a goodly number of pumping stations in Eastern England and the West Country. It could be that the Erith works were at full stretch at the time and the Norwich firm, nothing loath, avidly agreed to work to a competitor's design. The condenser was in tandem behind the low pressure cylinder and the cut-off could be varied by hand to suit the load. Cylinders were 9¾in and 16in x 21in, the ratio of piston areas being 2.7 : 1 and the normal rpm varied from 60 to 78 depending upon the lift being dealt with by the pump. The author was able to test this engine in 1941 when the maximum recorded ihp was 28.212, the pump delivering against a lift of 3ft 9½in. As few indicator diagrams seem to be available these days, I include a set seen in Fig 245 illustrating how important such diagrams are in showing any defects or irregularities etc. In this case the

Fig 244 Single cylinder grasshopper by Riches & Watts.

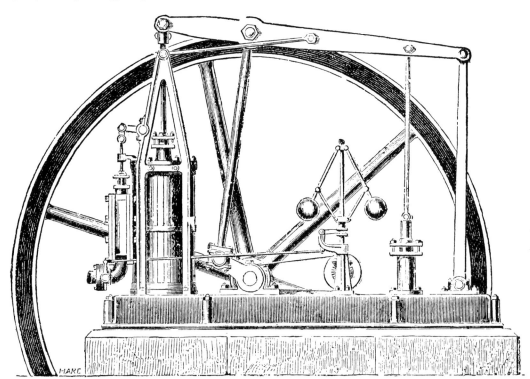

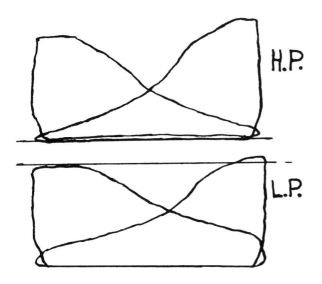

Fig 245 Indicator diagrams from a large Riches & Watts horizontal pumping engine.

Fig 246 View of the engine mentioned in Fig 245 together with the gearing to the turbine pump.

back end of the HP cylinder was receiving steam at a slightly lower pressure than the front, which small fault was subsequently rectified. The LP diagrams are excellent and indicate very little back pressure on the return stroke, the vacuum gauge showing 27.8in of mercury. A general view of this fine engine is recorded in Fig 246, which also illustrates the massive gearing to

the turbine pump but sad to relate all is now destroyed.

In 1865 the Duke's Palace Ironworks showed a single cylinder traction engine at the Norwich RAS Show that year but little information concerning its details have been discovered. It is fairly certain that the 8 nhp portable single cylinder block was used on this road engine. It does appear, however, that traction engines were not persevered with, probably on account of other competitors in this class of engine and their other types being in greater demand. In consequence nothing more was heard of it.

During the last years Riches & Co. carried out modifications and improvements to existing engines, with less accent on the production of new ones. A good example of this work was new governor cut-off gear fitted to an early beam engine in 1896, working in Cooper's Biscuit Factory in King Street, Norwich, the site now being Read's Flour Mills.

On many of their large engines Riches & Watts fitted their own design of shaft governor to control the point of cut-off. It is shown diagramatically in Fig 247 where A is a disc rotating on the crankshaft B while C is the eccentric. DD are two weights carried on rods joined at one end to the eccentric and at the other sliding in guides FF. It will be seen that as the disc rotates the weights DD will fly further and further from the centre, compressing the springs JJ and so pulling the eccentric round the sheave, this altering the travel of the valve, and therefore the point of cut-off.

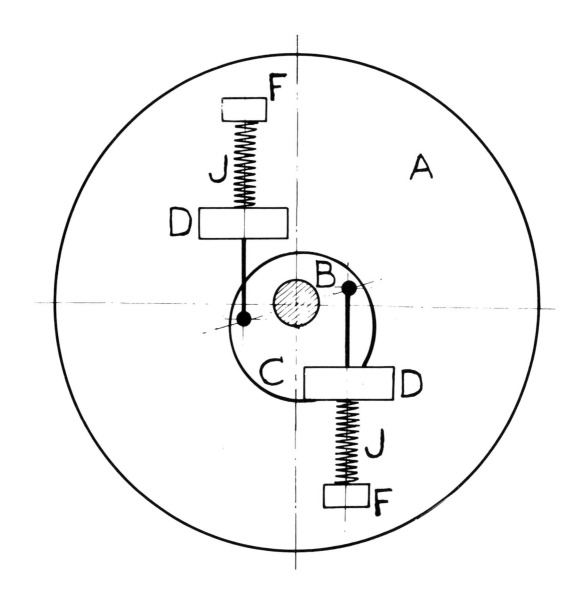

Fig 247 Diagrammatic details of the Riches & Watts shaft governor.

Although never illustrated in their publications, Riches & Watts designed and made an attractive-looking direct-acting steam pump with the steam cylinder 6in x 7in arranged vis-à-vis with the pump cylinder, the plunger being 2¼in diameter, and the complete unit is to be seen in Fig 248. The connecting rod is short and driven only on one side, as will be seen, the flywheel in this case being needed solely to continue motion over dead centres. This uncommon unit after salvage by the author is now preserved in the Bridewell Museum, Norwich.

In conclusion I deem it appropriate to illustrate in Fig 249 (page 158) one of this maker's circular nameplates, all of which were remembered for their fine and artistic lettering.

Fig 248 The vis-à-vis steam pump by Riches & Watts.

Fig 249 Some elegant Riches & Watts nameplates.

XXXII

SABBERTON BROTHERS,
St. Martin at Palace Ironworks, NORWICH.

A very old established firm commenced by Thomas Sabberton of Thorpe, near Norwich, and his four sons who claim to have supplied plant for the Norwich-Yarmouth railway line in 1845, and later in 1884, castings for Foundry Bridge, Norwich, which was erected by Robert Tidman & Sons (see No XXXVIII). In 1875 they were classified as "Boilermakers and Engineers Mechanical" and again so as late as 1896. They finally closed down the foundry and engine building side of the business in 1923 and the firm now trades under the title Bussey & Sabberton Brothers Ltd. which forms an extensive motor and garage complex.

Thomas Sabberton and his sons entered the steam engine trade in the late 1870s and among the first engines they made were some high speed vertical jobs having a cylinder 6in x 6in, one of which is shown in Fig 250. Many were supplied to Paris & Scott (see No XXII) when this firm had the Old Gothic Works in King Street, Norwich. Messrs. Paris & Scott coupled these Sabberton engines direct to generators of their own make, both combined on a common bedplate. They were commonly known as the "Norwich Ship Lighters", their normal speed being usually up to 450 rpm. A larger but slower running example had a 10in x 8in cylinder and like many engines of this type had the cylinder supported on four columns.

Several tandem compound engines left the works in the 1890s, one of which went to Messrs. A. J. Caley Ltd. Norwich, the well known manufacturing confectioners, but it has long since been broken up. A large vertical was made for Messrs. Harmers of St. Andrews, Norwich, but this too is now gone. Another horizontal engine with a single cylinder was made for and supplied to the City Laundry, Norwich, but unhappily this also has gone.

A few small launch engines were among others made, one of which was fitted in a river steamer called *Golden Arrow*. Another with duplex cylinders 7½in x 10in was installed in the *Christine*, 53 feet long built at Brightlingsea in 1867. Later, Sabberton Brothers made for and fitted in the steam ketch *Cheshire Cat* a small compound engine with cylinders 5½in and 10in x 8in. The ketch was built at Littlehampton in 1889. It is very unfortunate that no illustrations of the above marine engines have been discovered to show their main details. Some of the firm's records were destroyed by enemy action in 1942.

An interesting item of engineering history arises from the type of engine seen in Fig 250. We shall notice that ultimately G. E. Hawes & Son acquired the

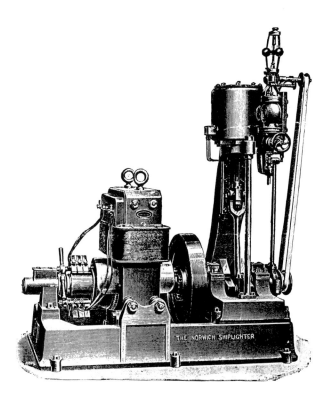

Fig 250 Sabberton Brothers small vertical engine.

foundry of Sturgess & Towlson when they made castings for school furniture. Messrs. Colman & Glendenning in their works at the back of St. Stephen's Street used many such castings and exhibited finished school desks, seats and so on in their showroom's windows in Orford Hill. Colman & Glendenning also sold Sabberton vertical engines, perhaps the only case of steam engines being on display in a shop window in the whole of Eastern England. The late Lt. Col. S. E. Glendenning has told me that when a small boy he remembers vividly seeing these engines in the windows of his father's firm.

XXXIII

SAVAGES LTD.,
St. Nicholas Ironworks, KING'S LYNN.

Frederick Savage was born on 3rd March 1828 in the village of Hevingham, Norfolk, near the small country town of Aylsham, and attended the village school. At the tender age of ten years he got a job with Mr. J. Dye, hurdle maker, established on the estate of Robert Marsham. When aged sixteen he entered the employment of Thomas Cooper, Whitesmith and Machine Maker, in Theatre Street, East Dereham. On Cooper's death the business came into the ownership of John and James Gill, Millwrights and Machine Makers, where young Savage gained experience in implement design and manufacture. He made another move shortly afterwards, this time to Holmes & Son, Prospect Place Works, Castle Hill, Norwich, who again were Implement Makers and General Engineers.

It was while he was in the city that he met and married Susannah Bloyce of Tuttington, the couple being married in St. James Church, Norwich, on 26th August 1850. Whilst working in Norwich, Savage had saved some money and moved with his wife to Lynn some time in 1851. Here he took up the post of foreman carpenter with Charles Willett who had premises in Lynn High Street and in Baker Lane. Willett was somewhat of a pluralist being described as Tinplate Worker, Whitesmith, wholesale and retail Ironmonger, Brazier and Bell-Hanger. An excellent chance for a young man to widen his experience! Among those working at Willets at that time were some young apprentices, Alfred Dodman, Joseph Turner and James Bunting. Years later Joseph Bunting and his brothers Thomas and Robert joined Frederick Savage and stayed with him for many years.

Charles Willett surrendered his tenancy of the Baker Lane property c1853 making Frederick Savage redundant, so the latter commenced on his own account with a small forge in Tower Street at the Mermaid & Fountain Yard. Naturally he kept to products he knew such as small agricultural implements and succeeded well enough to acquire other premises in Station Street. Then, again in 1860, he moved to another site in St. Nicholas Street, the entrance being on a corner of the Tuesday Market Place and this he called St. Nicholas Ironworks.

As his business expanded so the need for larger premises increased and in 1873 Savage rented nine acres of partially-reclaimed land on the north side of Lynn from Sir Lewis Jarris, the banker. Here the new St. Nicholas Ironworks was erected. The business thus continued under the old title of Frederick Savage, Engineer until 1893, when it was converted into a joint stock association entitled Frederick Savage & Co. Ltd. After Frederick's death on 27th April 1897 his two surviving sons, Frederick William and John Thomas, reorganised the concern and called it Savage Brothers

Fig 251 Frederick Savage's early portable engine.

Fig 252 Savage's later portable.

Limited. However, in 1910 the business was declared insolvent so a receiver was invited to take charge. He solved the problem by inviting several local worthies and business men to form a consortium and they purchased outright the faltering Company and all its assets. By 1911 the deal was complete, the new title of the firm being Savages Limited.

Savages Limited continued in business with the showmen and during World War 2 were responsible for a great variety of work covering such jobs as ship repairs, maintenance of other important firm's plant to keep them going, the manufacture of certain types of pressure vessels, tanks, crystallizers and so on, and additionally repairs to all types of boilers. Naturally the foundry was continually in production of a great range of castings. However, by the late 1960s the directors felt their ages and so on 31st March 1973 St. Nicholas Ironworks finally closed down and the site has now been cleared and new structures for modern factory units erected.

It is very relevant to record that Frederick Savage was for some years a JP and Mayor of Lynn Regis in the years 1889 and 1890. His monument nigh unto the

South Gates was unveiled on 27th May 1892 and it is Lynn's only statue to a public man.

Probably Savage's first engine may have been a portable built during his sojourn in Tower Street and one of these early engines is shown in Fig 251. The square chimney base, crankshaft-driven feed pump and wooden wheels are typical features of most English portable engines at this period. Made in several sizes, the most popular were of 7 and 8 nhp.

Over the years the type was modified and improved to the state illustrated in Fig 252, where the cylinder is now well lagged, spring-loaded safety valves have taken the place of the weight and lever type valve and a high speed Pickering type governor substituted for the pendulus and un-loaded Watt form of instrument. Such portables were made in 4–10 nhp with a single and 10–12 nhp with duplex cylinders.

A natural development from the portable was the stationary semi-portable or overtype shown in Fig 253. Without wheels, the front end was supported on a hollow cast iron box serving also as a water tank to

161

Fig 253 The Savage semi-portable.

Fig 254 Savage's single cylinder horizontal engine.

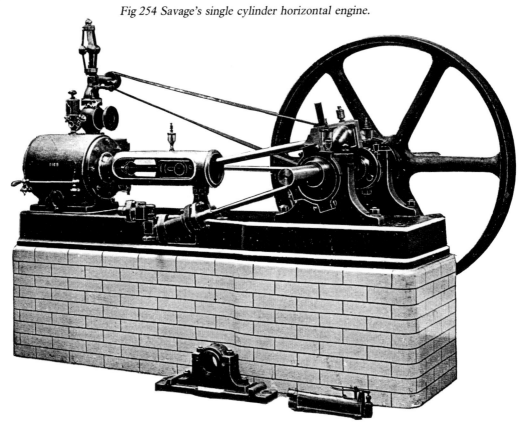

which the feed and return pipes are connected. They were made with a single cylinder from 4–10 nhp only.

The most popular stationary engine at this time was the ordinary horizontal and the Savage example is included in Fig 254. Obviously where possible the cylinder and motion common to the portable and semi-portables were used thus saving production costs and pattern making.

Lynn being one of the ancient ports it was only natural therefore that Savages would have marine associations and so we find they could supply a series of simple steam winches as illustrated in Fig 255. Embodying single and double purchase motions the ratios were 4½ and 9 : 1. The main shaft carried a central barrel and warping ends with the whipping drums on the ends of the second motion shaft. Shipping handles could be used for working by hand if ever necessary. The duplex cylinders varied from 4in x 9in to 8in x 12in. Note that Savages, unlike many of their competitors, clothed the cylinder barrels with lagging.

Although Frederick Savage's fame rests mainly on his fairground machinery he and his establishment made a worthy contribution to the early development of the self-moving road engine. Unfortunately authentic records of the first hundred or so of Savage engines have, with one exception, not been found and therefore much of what has been published in recent years is unreliable. However, newspaper statements record a self-moving engine of his make travelling from one of the Terringtons to Lynn on 16th July 1858, having been supplied about that time to a local farmer. Un-

fortunately no photograph, sketch or drawing has survived or been discovered so any illustration would be purely conjecture. Although I have previously quoted elsewhere the *Norfolk Chronicle's* word painting of the occasion, it is worth repeating:– *"The glare, the rumbling and the puffing and snorting of this novel train as at night it passed along the highways and especially in the town, created as may be supposed no little wonder and excitement"*. Over 120 years later excitement and wonder are to be discovered still on the A17 but of quite a different kind!

By the 1860s Savage was producing traction engines and one of these early examples is seen in Fig 256 complete with small tender, towing a threshing machine and elevator. These engines were of light

Fig 255 The Savage steam winch.

Fig 256 Engraving of a Savage-built threshing train.

Fig 257 Nearside view of F. Savage on his chain engine.

construction and one or two had wooden wheels similar to those on the first portables. Later, cast iron wheels succeeded wood wheels and one such is shown in Fig 257. The driver is reputed to be the maker, the background being some part of the Tuesday Market Place. An offside view of the same class is seen in Fig 258 but with the chain drive on the offside.

A larger version of Savage's chain engine is depicted in Fig 259 where for longer distances an extra well tank for water is fitted beneath the boiler and front steerage is still used. The Savage final design of chain engine is to be seen in Fig 260 where steerage from the manstand is now provided and which arrangement was to continue until road engines ceased to be made at St. Nicholas Ironworks.

Following the chain engines there came the engines with all-gear transmission and one of this design is included in Fig 261. They were large engines having an overall width of 8ft 6in, overall height of 9ft 4in and an overall length of 18 feet. One of 10 nhp had a cylinder 10in x 12in and when belt driving ran at 150 rpm. They had two road speeds and weighed about 13 tons in

Fig 258 Offside prospect of an engine similar to that in Fig 257.

working order. Savage called them the *Agriculturist* to imply diversity of uses in agriculture. They were exhibited at and won various medals in Shows at Thetford, Kingston-Upon-Hull, Gainsborough, Bedford and Long Sutton during the 1870s.

At this period most firms had evolved and improved the traction engine into a form which has become familiar today and Savage's next achievement is shown in Fig 262 where all wheels are built up from mild steel sections. Note the front axle set well back and attached to the boiler barrel. This reduced the wheelbase, facilitating turning into gateways and negotiating similar hazards. With their twin Salter safety valves and elegantly proportioned Watt-type governor to name but two features, they were most attractive-looking engines. Savage called this design his *Sandringham* engine. He was a devout believer in the Monarchy and with the then reigning Sovereign interested in the parish of Sandringham it was a loyal and happy thought to name his product after her. I can only trust Her Majesty was suitably impressed!

Both the *Agriculturist* and *Sandringham* engines had two speeds incorporated in the transmission as standard but both could be fitted with the maker's patent slow motion gear made under his Patent

Also adapted for Thrashing, Grinding, &c., with wrought iron road gear link motion, steel pinions, reversing gear, and all the most recent improvements, FOR PRICES SEE PAGE 11.

Fig 259 The enlarged chain engine from St. Nicholas Works.

Fig 260 The final form of Savage chain road engine.

Fig 261 Savage's Agriculturist traction engine.

Fig 262 The Sandringham class Savage road engine.

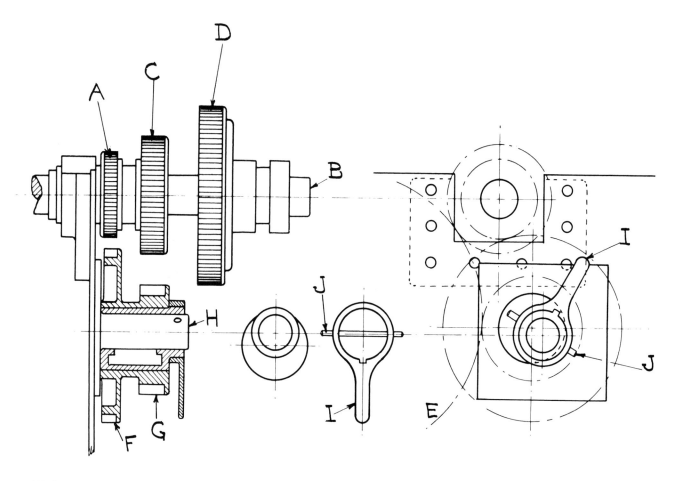

Fig 263 Savage's slow motion gear drawing.

No 1457 of 1873. The gear is shown diagrammatically in Fig 263 where A is a small pinion of 12 teeth fixed permanently to the crankshaft B near to the cannon bracket. C and D are the standard low and high speed pinions respectively and E represents the pitch circle of the low speed gear of the spur-ring. F and G comprise the two pinions of the patent slow speed gear and which are fitted eccentrically on to the short stub spindle H fixed rigidly by means of the square flange to the hornplate. These pinions F and G have 35 and 15 teeth respectively, the pitch of F and A being slightly less than the others. When out of gear the hand lever I is as shown in the details and all the driver has to do to engage the slow motion gear is to turn the lever I into the position shown in the elevation and lock it with the pin J through the stub shaft. This turning of the eccentric centre mounting engages the larger pinion F and A and the small pinion G with E. Before moving the lever I the driver must move the ordinary speed pinions C and D into neutral when neither of them mesh with the spur-ring. The nett effect is to introduce an extra low ratio into the train of gears making three speeds in all. Taking an actual *Sandringham* class engine, having

crankshaft gears of 12 and 21 teeth, spur-ring of 65 and 74 teeth, and final drive pinion and gear of 16 and 63 teeth respectively, the low speed ratio would be:–

$$\frac{12 \times 16}{74 \times 63} = 24.28 \text{ to } 1.$$

The high speed ratio will be :–

$$\frac{21 \times 6}{65 \times 63} = 12.18 \text{ to } 1.$$

Bringing into action the slow motion gear gives an emergency low ratio therefore of :–

$$\frac{12 \times 15 \times 16}{35 \times 74 \times 63} = \frac{32}{1813} = 56.65 \text{ to } 1.$$

The three illustrations in Fig 264 will help still further to explain this mechanism where the first shows the gear out of action, the second shows it in operation and the third is an end view on all seven wheels. For

168

Fig 264 The slow motion gear on an engine.

additional interest there is included in Fig 265 a general arrangement drawing of one of these famous old engines having twin spring loaded safety valves whereas the earlier *Sandringham* engines had twin Salter type valves.

The basis of the ordinary English traction engine was the boiler forming the chassis, one may say which was subjected to various additional and at times, severe stresses extra to those incidental to it acting primarily as a pressure vessel. Referring now to Fig 266 it will be seen that the hornplates being in four pieces were both part of the outer firebox and yet separate. To accommodate the back axle the two outer firebox casing plates were extended rearwards and a suitably curved plate was fitted to the outer crown plate each side and bored to take the crank and countershaft bearings. In this way the screwed stays were relieved of some of the stresses set up by the first and second shafts and had to withstand only those stresses set up by the rear axle. The firebox outer casing plates were therefore free to "breathe" or accommodate themselves to expansion, contraction and loading. Fig 267 shows very clearly these independent plates. Support for the inner crown plate is provided by the three bridge stays shown. The pressure on the plate is taken by the five bolts in each bridge, through the bridge itself and on to the bridge ends supported on the tube and back plates so these two plates are loaded "on edge". Viewed as a structure, such

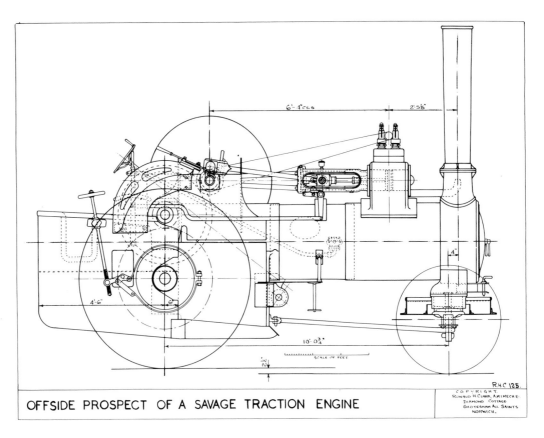

COPYRIGHT.
Ronald H.Clark, A.M.I.Mech.E.
Diamond Cottage
Ghotesham All Saints
Norwich.

OFFSIDE PROSPECT OF A SAVAGE TRACTION ENGINE

Fig 265 Drawing of the side view of a Savage geared engine.

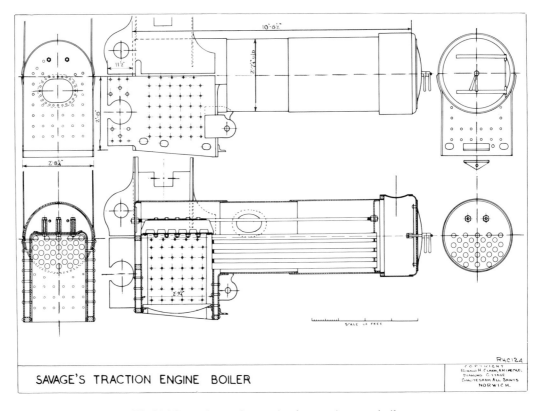

COPYRIGHT.
Ronald H.Clark, A.M.I.Mech.E.
Diamond Cottage
Ghotesham All Saints
Norwich.

SAVAGE'S TRACTION ENGINE BOILER

Fig 266 Savage's traction engine locomotive type boiler.

170

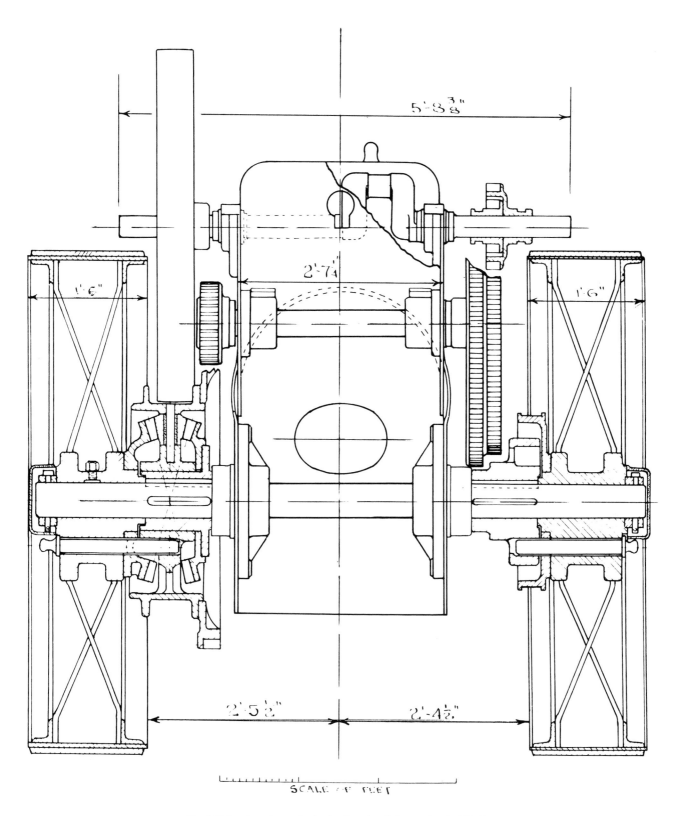

Fig 267 Section through the back axle of the engine in Fig 265.

an arrangement is enormously strong, the objection being the cavities between the five bolts in which scale always seems to collect in greater quantities than elsewhere. Two 1¼in diameter longitudinal ties tied the backhead and the front tubeplate together. The shell in two strakes is 2ft 7¼in smallest outside diameter and there are 30 tubes x 2½in diameter x 6ft 3in long, the dimensions for the 8 nhp being proportionately larger. The compensating gear or differential is combined with the winding drum and two speeds were provided in the gearing giving ratios of 12.17 : 1 and 24.2 : 1. An offside view of a typical Savage engine is shown in Fig 268 illustrating No 464 preserved in North Norfolk, probably the only traction engine of this make remaining.

Details of the cylinder, a most important item in any engine, is depicted in the drawing in Fig 269 which also shows how the twin Salter safety valves are fitted. Usually, the English makers made their 8 nhp cylinders of 9in bore but for goodly measure Frederick Savage made his 9⅛in bore.

Fig 268 A late Savage road engine at work.

Some readers may be acquainted with Stephenson's Link Motion, at least in theory, but how it is set out for a commercially successful engine is illustrated in Fig 270. I believe at the present time it is not the fashion for seats of learning to provide any tuition on the steam engine which may account for why from time to time I receive requests for the proportions of Stephenson's Valve Gear. The Savage mechanism is an example of this gear applied to an engine. To augment the drawing I include the scantlings as follow:-

Radius of Link	3ft 4½in
Length of curved slot measured along the centreline	8⅛in
Ratio of length of slot to radius of links	1 : 5
Radius of rods	3ft 2⅝in
Valve travel	2½in
Throw of eccentrics	1¼in
Angle of advance	30°

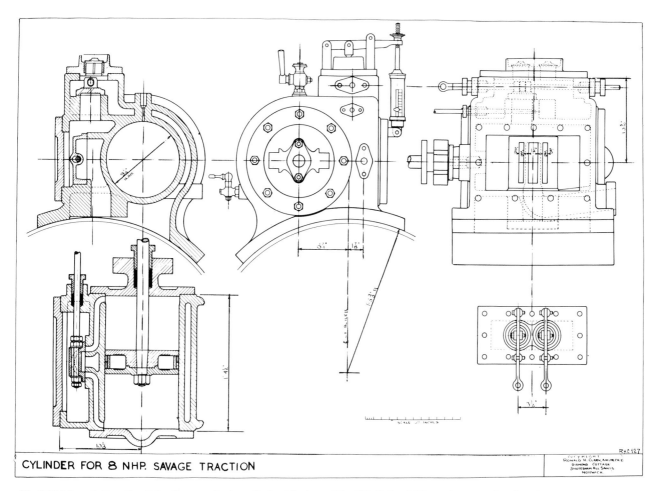

CYLINDER FOR 8 NHP. SAVAGE TRACTION

Fig 269 (above) Details of the Savage single cylinder block.   *Fig 270 (below) The valve gear fitted to Savage road engines.*

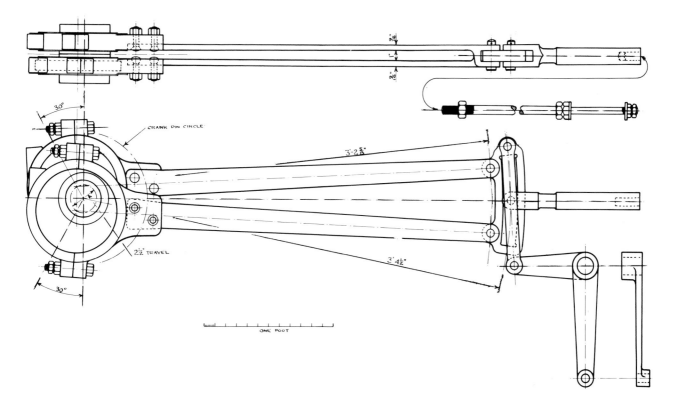

During building, the forwards eccentric was fitted next to the crank with its rod at the bottom of the link. In the earlier chain engines we have noticed this procedure was reversed. An interesting point of this design was that only one keyway was cut in the crankshaft to drive the two eccentrics and the keyway was long enough to include the governor pulley.

Coming now to the compound engines we have in Fig 271 details of the firm's 7 nhp cylinder block, the cylinders being 5½in and 9½in x 10in. As in the Burrell design the high pressure cylinder is on the right-hand side, the transfer passage also acting as a small receiver and being subject to boiler steam provides an amount of inter-stage re-heat conducive to steam economy. This double crank compound block was fitted apparently exclusively to the showman's engines and a typical example, No 730 named *Empress*, is shown in Fig 272. Known as a traction centre engine, it had the top turret and gear superimposed above the boiler and formed a secure centre about which the roundabout was built up. The top lantern wheel was driven by a vertical shaft in turn bevel driven off the crankshaft and this drive could be clutched in and out of gear. This arrangement can be seen perhaps more clearly in Fig 273 where it is applied to a single cylinder showman's engine No 728 named

Fig 272 Empress – a most famous Savage road locomotive No 730.

Enterprise. Although a single cylinder machine I think it fits into place appropriately amongst the showground engines. These two engines, Nos 728 and 730, both left

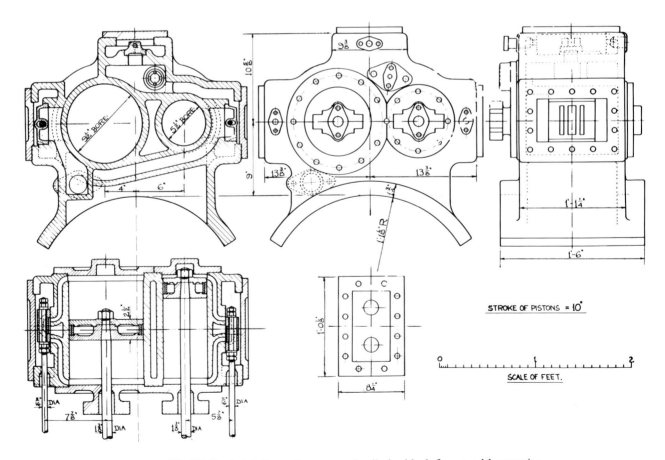

Fig 271 Frederick Savage's compound cylinder block for a road locomotive.

Fig 273 Another famous Savage production, the traction centre engine Enterprise.

Fig 274 The annular compound single crank road engine from St. Nicholas Works, Lynn.

the works new in 1898, No 728 going to Baker and No 730 to Barker, Thurston & Sons.

Perhaps the most interesting road engine Savages ever made was No 614 of 7 nhp, built in 1894 for Jacob Studt, the famous showman and illustrated in Fig 274. At first glance it could be mistaken for a single cylinder machine but a study of Fig 275 shows the most unusual arrangement where the low pressure cylinder is an annulus outside the high pressure thus giving it the name "annular compound". There are, of course, three piston rods uniting on to a common crosshead, the connecting rod being attached in the centre. The slide valve is hollow to admit high pressure steam to the low pressure through ports cast in the end covers, the inner ports – for the low pressure – being set out in the usual way and with the conventional exhaust port in the centre. In this example of 7 nhp the high pressure cylinder was 6in diameter, the low pressure 7⅞in and 12⅞in with a stroke of 12in. Centres of low pressure piston rods 10¼in. Ratio of piston areas 2·94 : 1.

An overhead oblique view on to the top of this unusual engine is included in Fig 276 where the three piston rods and single connecting rod are easily studied together with the location of the twin Salter safety

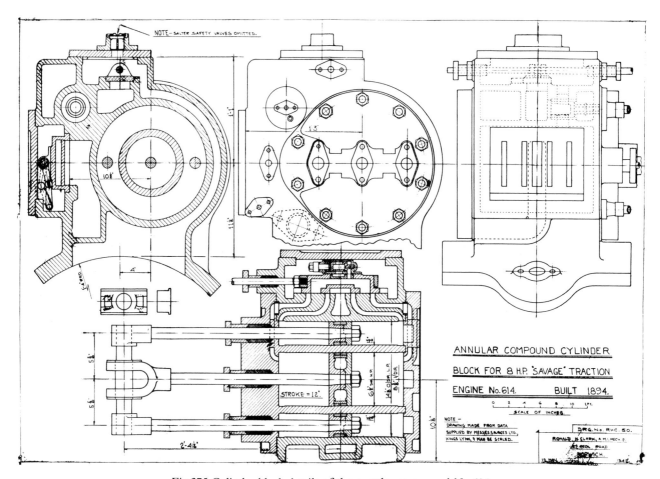

Fig 275 Cylinder block details of the annular compound No 614.

valves, and the spring loaded Watt-type governor for use when belt driving. After nearly thirty years continuous use the second owners in Norfolk required a new cylinder block but the pattern could not be found so a replacement single cylinder was fitted instead. Ironically, years later the original annular compound pattern was unearthed in the extensive pattern store!

Altogether three such engines were made, the other two being of 8 nhp where the high pressure cylinder was 6½in diameter and the low pressure 8⅜in and 14⅛in diameters, again with a stroke of 12in. The centres of the low pressure piston rods was 11¼in. Ratio of piston areas 3·06:1. The working pressure was 140 psi in all three cases.

This annular compound was, of course, one form of single crank compound and another practical and interesting Savage example was the tandem arrangement of cylinders seen in the drawing in Fig 277. Here the cylinders are arranged "in tandem" and are 5½in and 8in x 10in, the unit being for a light type of road engine and dated 1895, to use steam at 120 or 150 psi. There is little startling about the tandem layout of cylinders but the ingenuity here lies in the transference of steam from the high pressure to the low pressure

cylinder, and this was effected by using a piston valve for the high pressure with outside admission. Exhaust was by a ring of ports and then through the hollow valve rod and out through another ring of rectangular orifices into the low pressure valve chest. Admission into and out of the low pressure cylinder was controlled by the slide valve in the usual way. The valve rod was polished externally and as only 1½in of it was exposed at any one moment the loss of heat due to radiation was particularly small. Great care was taken so that the rings were free in their grooves but with no side play. Apparently this accuracy was found to be equally necessary by the petrol engine makers and was hailed as a new discovery!

Yet another design of Savage cylinder block designed in 1908 is included in Fig 278 where the cylinders are duplex, each being 6¼in x 12in. Both valve chests housed a piston valve 4in diameter, the ports being similar to those of their slide valve engines. To supply the two high pressure cylinders with sufficient steam, the firm's largest locomotive type boiler was used, the shell having an external diameter of 2ft 4in. A general arrangement outline drawing is shown in Fig 279, the engine being completed in January 1909, numbered 847

Fig 276 View on the motion of the annular Savage compound.

and delivered to the famous showman P. Collins. Although unusual in having no dynamo bracket, it did have the refinement of a feed water heater between the cylinder block and chimney. With both cylinders being high pressure and the cranks at 90° there would be four exhaust beats per revolution, sounds suggestive of a railway locomotive. Incidentally, this interesting engine bore the name *The Wonder* for many years.

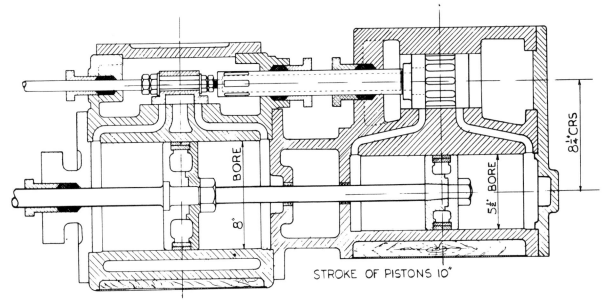

Fig 277 Savage's tandem compound cylinder block.

Fig 278 The duplex cylinder arrangement by F. Savage.

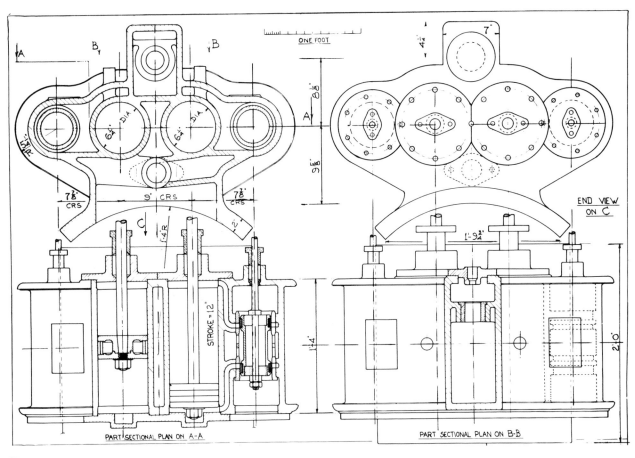

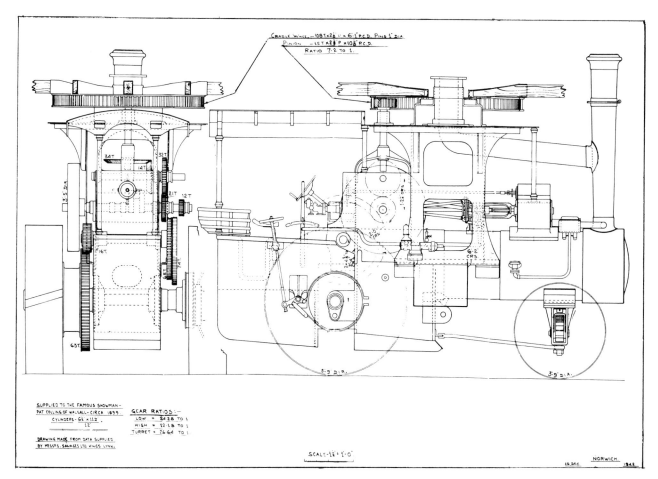

Fig 279 Another well-known Savage production,
The Wonder.

Frederick Savage was also interested in cultivation by steam but when designing his first engines he refrained from subjecting the poor boiler to extra incalculable stresses due to attaching the winding drum to, and beneath it. He avoided this by coiling the cables inside the deep hollow rims of the rear of the engine thus leaving them free to rotate, the idea being depicted in Fig 280. When travelling on the road the cables were protected by detachable cover plates. In Fig 280 the cylinder was arranged at the front or smokebox end of the boiler which later became standard practice although in Fig 281 we have an alternative design where the cylinder is mounted over the firebox. An offside view of the first type is illustrated in Fig 282. Note the detachable tread plates piled underneath the boiler. Just how this ploughing system was set out is shown in the charming panoramic view in Fig 283.

At one period Frederick Savage was very interested in the Darby Digger and may have constructed about four of these machines. They were rather ponderous as may be seen from Fig 284, but which shows clearly how the digging forks were actuated by the gear and bevel drives taking power from the two cross shafts, in turn

Fig 280 Savage cultivating engine with drums in the
rear wheels.

179

Fig 281 The alternative cultivating engine with cylinder at the firebox end.

Fig 282 Side view of a Savage ploughing engine with cover plates.

bevel-driven off the crankshaft. The unusual boiler had a central firebox, rather after the Fairlie arrangement, with a smokebox and chimney each end. The single cylinder was 9⅛in x 12in using steam at 120 psi. When

digging, the great machine moved slowly sideways across the field, but for travelling on the road the two pairs of road wheels were turned through 90° and the outfit progressed with one chimney first. The width dug

Fig 283 Charming woodcut showing plan of ploughing.

Fig 284 The Darby-Savage well-known Digger.

Fig 285 Little Samson, the Savage design of steam motor tractor.

was 21 feet, the tines penetrating to a depth of 9in x 10in and about 0.65 to 1.19 of an acre could be cultivated per hour depending upon the type of soil to be dug.

Thomas Churchward Darby established a small works in Pleshy near Chelmsford in 1862 to produce his horse hoe patent of 1858. Following his horse he evolved his famous digger but got the heavier parts built out by such firms as Eddington & Steevenson of Chelmsford, J. & H. McLaren of Leeds and Frederick Savage.

This Darby Digger was perhaps one of the most interesting and ingenious steam engines made in Norfolk.

In company with many other English engineers at the relevant time Savage Brothers Limited tackled the steam motor tractor and their product is depicted in Fig 285 which shows it to have been a neat and well proportioned little engine known as *Little Samson*. Although the single cylinder was only 6in x 9in, *Little Samsons* have been known to shift two loaded furniture pantechnicons. A solid flywheel was used and the gearing tidily enclosed. Further details are to be seen in the drawing illustrated in Fig 286. It is not known precisely how many *Little Samsons* were made during the years 1910–1913 but from drawings and dates thereon the total may have been about seven. One constructed in 1910 was sent to Norway and had a non-standard cylinder 6½in x 9in. Another was used by the showman J. Murphy for several years and this had the

refinement of a rear mounted pillar crane used for mounting round-about vehicles. The method of fitting is seen in Fig 287.

In order to secure low fuel consumption a number of Savage engines had fitted an exhaust feed water heater of simple construction as illustrated in Fig 288. The cold boiler feed passed through the tubes which were surrounded by the low pressure exhaust steam. The makers stated that use of the heater could bring haulage costs down to as little as 1½d per ton per mile just prior to 1914.

In considering road engines there remain the Savage-built steam wagons. Savage Brothers became interested in this class of steam vehicle when the patterns, drawings and goodwill of Messrs. C. & A. Musker Ltd. of The Brook, Liverpool, became available when they gave up this side of their business in 1905. Muskers had first produced wagons in 1900 and were already well-known engineers. Musker's boiler was of the water tube type but was improved by Savage Brothers drawing office and into the form delineated in Fig 289, where it is important to note that the tube ends are all straight where they are expanded into the tubeplate at the bottom and at the main stream drum at the top, thus facilitating production and reducing costs. Dry, hot steam was taken from the smaller top drum shown in the drawing. This improved Lynn boiler had 90 square feet of heating surface, the grate area being four square feet. Working pressure was 200 psi, the work's test pressure being 400 psi.

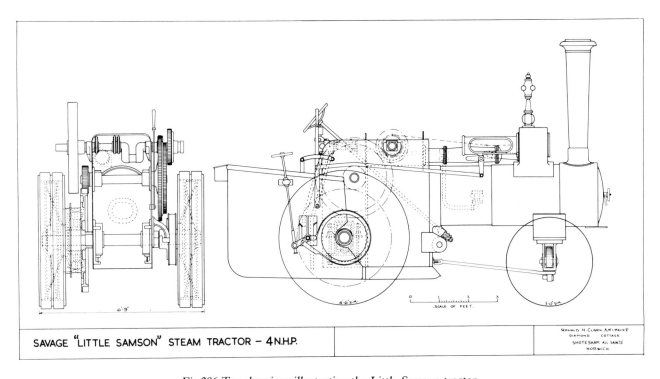

SAVAGE "LITTLE SAMSON" STEAM TRACTOR – 4 N.H.P.

RONALD H. CLARK A.M.I.MECH.E
DIAMOND COTTAGE
SHOTESHAM ALL SAINTS
NORWICH

Fig 286 Two drawings illustrating the Little Samson tractor.

Fig 287 The Little Samson tractor with rear crane.

Savage Brothers made five classes of wagon viz. OA, A, A1, B and C. Class OA used the original Musker boiler at first where the heating surface was 80 square feet and the grate area 3·19 square feet. Apparently only two Class OAs were made, as will be seen from the list in Appendix A. All the class As had a horizontal compound totally-enclosed engine with cylinders 4in and 7in x 5in with a piston valve to each cylinder. What the complete lorry looked like is to be seen in Fig 290 where the unusual load is a bronze statue of King Edward VII en route to Lynn grammar school. The compactness of the water tube boiler is clearly apparant.

Some vehicles used the Savage design of special locomotive type boiler depicted in the drawing in Fig 291. The first went through the boiler shop in January 1905. The total heating surface was 75 square feet and the grate area 3½ square feet. The tubes totalled 55 x 1¾in outside diameter of which 13 were screwed stay tubes and the barrel was 2ft 4in diameter and 2ft 9in between tubeplates, the working pressure being 200 psi, but with a test pressure in this case of 450 psi. For the Class B lorries the engine was partly re-designed to use a piston valve to the high and a slide

Fig 288 Savage's feed water heater.

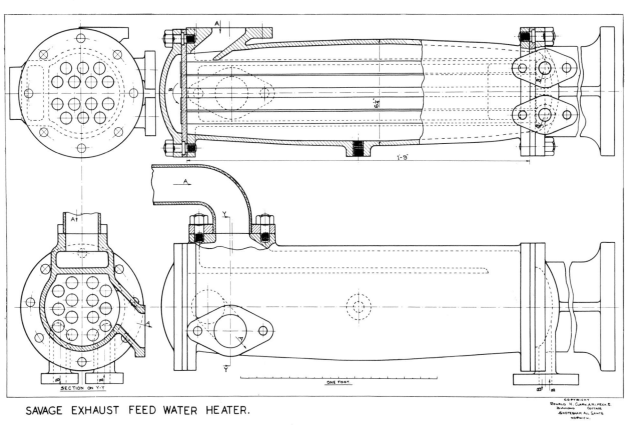

SAVAGE EXHAUST FEED WATER HEATER.

COPYRIGHT
RONALD H. CLARK A.M.I.MECH.E
DIAMOND COTTAGE
SHOTESHAM ALL SAINTS
NORWICH.

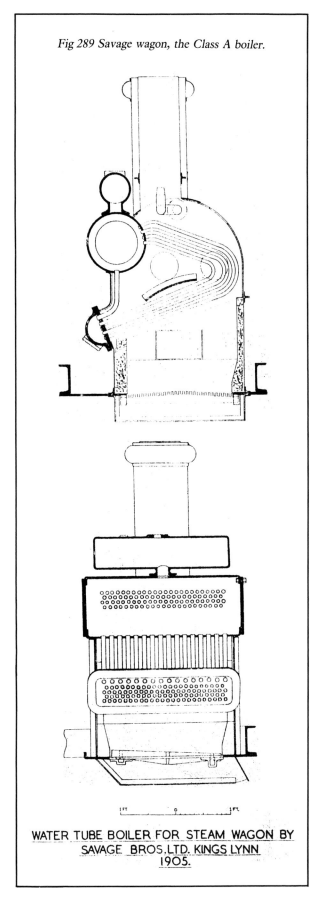

Fig 289 Savage wagon, the Class A boiler.

WATER TUBE BOILER FOR STEAM WAGON BY
SAVAGE BROS.LTD. KINGS LYNN
1905.

Fig 290 The Class A wagon completed.

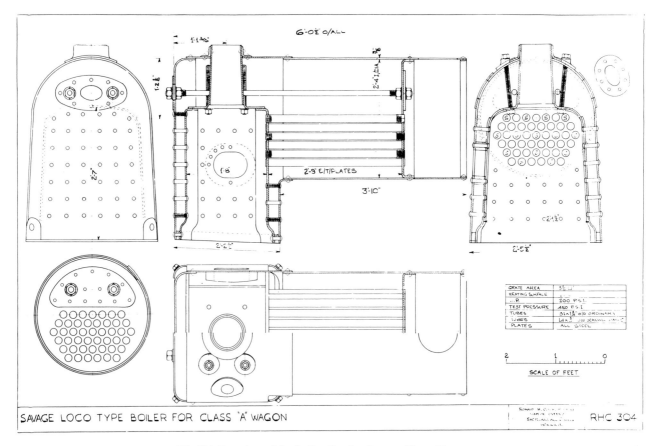

SAVAGE LOCO TYPE BOILER FOR CLASS 'A' WAGON

GRATE AREA	3½ □
HEATING SURFACE	
...P.	200 P.S.I
TEST PRESSURE	450 P.S.I
TUBES	31 × 1½" O/D ORDINARY
TUBES	14 × ¾" O/D SCREWED STAY-T
PLATES	ALL STEEL

RHC 304

Fig 291 Drawing of the boiler for the Savage Class A1 wagon.

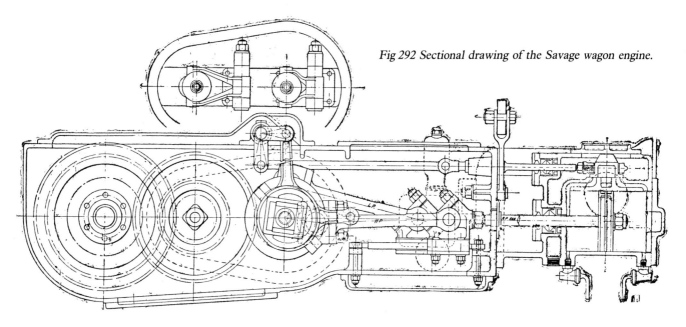

Fig 292 Sectional drawing of the Savage wagon engine.

valve to the low pressure cylinder, the cylinders now being 4½in and 7in x 7½in. A horizontal section through the low pressure cylinder is included in Fig 292. A Class A1 vehicle is to be seen in Fig 293 where it is fitted with a small dc generator aft of the driver's seat. For general contracting work it would be a

particularly useful unit. This wagon was exhibited at the Cordingley Show in 1906.

Class B wagons had the water tube boiler with a totally enclosed two-speed gearbox and Fig 294 shows a section through the final or third shaft carrying the rear chain sprockets; one must note also that this shaft runs

186

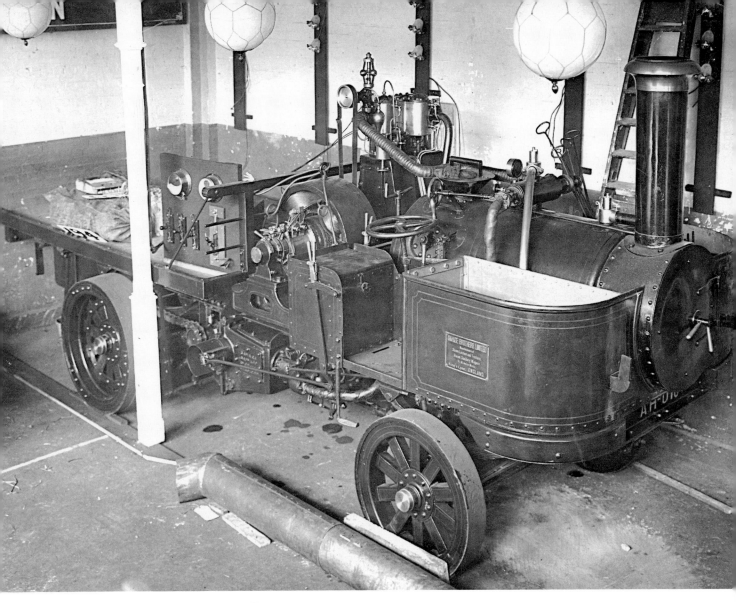

Fig 293 Alternative Class A1 wagon.

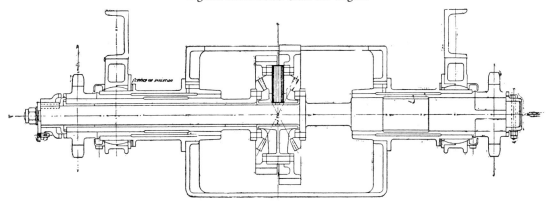

Fig 294 Drawing of the countershaft for the wagon.

in self-aligning bearings with spherical housing, then a very advanced feature. One of these Class B lorries won the Gold Medal in the Wagon Trials of 1907 and for many years the Medal was treasured in the director's office. It is now in Lynn Museum.

Lastly there was the Class C vehicles which the firm believed was the best of the series. It could use either the water tube boiler or a vertical boiler of their own design delineated in Fig 295. Overall this vertical boiler was only 2ft 6in diameter x 4ft 6½in long but possessed 63 square feet of heating surface with a grate area of 3·6 square feet and embodied 64 tubes 1½in outside

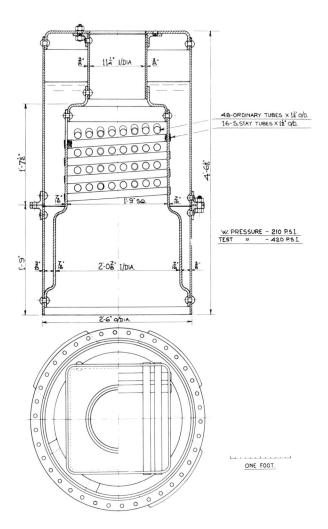

48-ORDINARY TUBES X 1¼" O/D.
16-S.STAY TUBES X 1½" O/D.

W. PRESSURE - 210 P.S.I.
TEST   "   - 420 P.S.I.

ONE FOOT.

Fig 295 Details of the Class C wagon vertical boiler.

diameter arranged in cross banks as shown. Steam was used in a new undermounted engine illustrated in Fig 296 where the compound cylinders were now 4⅛in and 7⅛in x 6in. An ingenious feature was the single eccentric reversing gear where one eccentric sufficed for both cylinders. Motion to the high pressure valve was provided by the upper end of the eccentric rod to the cross rocker shaft and thus to the bell-crank lever opposite the valve rod. The angle of the bell-crank was, of course, 90°, equal to the angle between the cranks. Motion to the low pressure valve was taken direct from the appropriate point in the eccentric rod. Reversing was simple but clever and effected by the control rod operating through the hollow crankshaft to a block working in straight slots cut at an angle in the shaft. Obviously as the block was moved longitudinally the angled slots caused it to rotate thus turning the eccentrics round the shaft a small amount which in turn altered the position of the valve.

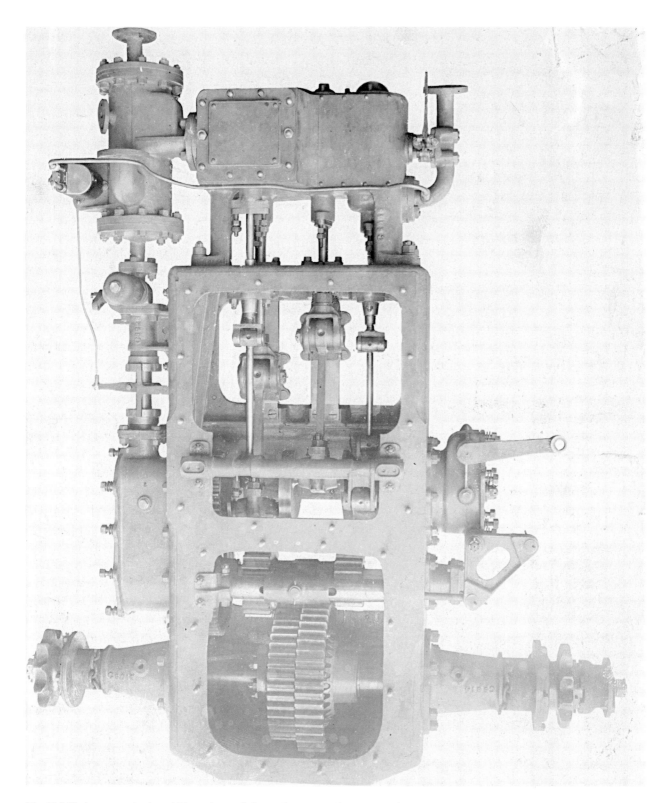

Fig 296 (facing page & above) Two views of the undermounted wagon engine.

Fig 297 (above) The later Class C Savage wagon and boiler for export.

Fig 298 (below) Savage wagon fitted for sanitary duties.

Some lorries were built for export and one for brazil is depicted in Fig 297. Others were equipped as sanitary and road-sweeping wagons and one such is to be seen outlined in Fig 298. The sanitary tank was fitted with a steam ejector for cesspool and gulley emptying. So when dear reader you see such an apparatus at work today reflect that it was being done over 70 years ago and without relying on imported fuel!

Savage Brothers evolved their patent wood block wheel seen in the drawing in Fig 299. The section through the wheel rim makes the method of fitting quite clear, and the hardwood blocks were of course, set endwise to the grain.

Probably today this Lynn firm is remembered mainly for its fairground machinery, especially the later steam-driven outfits. This aspect has been fully covered by some recent publications but here it is appropriate to deal with the engines applied to the many "rides" produced at St. Nicholas Works. Where the merry-go-round had its centre turret built as part of the centre engine driving it, the engine was arranged as in Fig 300. As will be noticed easily, the drive was taken by a pair of bevels from the crankshaft to a short vertical shaft carrying a small pinion at the top end driving the centre or hub of the rotating ride. In this example the engine was carried by its own truck on four iron shod wooden wheels, all apparent in Fig 300. Where the machine was designed to be erected separately, the centre engine was

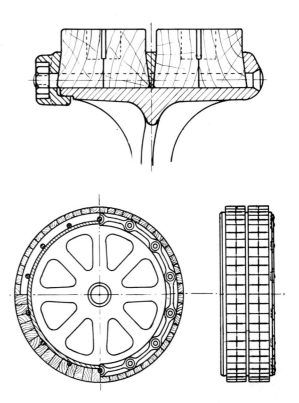

Fig 299 Wood block wheels fitted to some Savage steam wagons.

Fig 300 The Savage centre engine on its travelling truck.

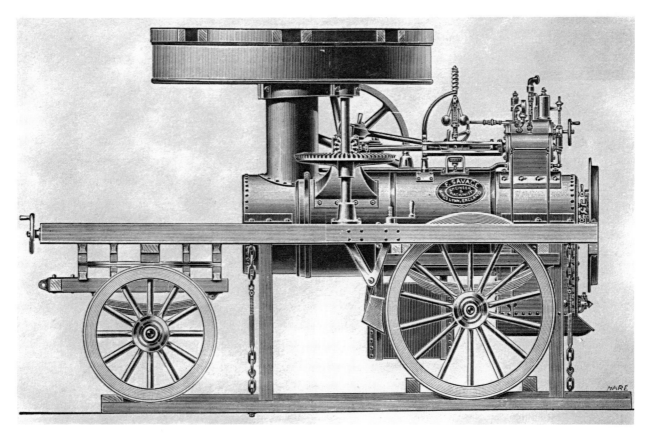

fixed transversely alongside the centre pole as in Fig 301, where the crankshaft was extended to take the drive via a set of bevels, the larger wheel being keyed to the base of the upright centre pole. In Fig 300 the centre pole was made to form the chimney but in Fig 301 the smoke went down the smokebox and along a horizontal flue to the base of the hollow pole.

All these centre engines had duplex cylinders with the valve chests back to back between the bores, a feature by which Savage engines can always be recognised. The cylinder sizes were as follow:–

Size 4   = 4¾in x 9in, also 4⅞in x 9in
Size 5   = 5⅛in x 9½in
Size 5½ = 3¾in x 7in
Size 6   = 4in x 8in

In Fig 302 there is illustrated a right-hand side view in a general arrangement drawing of a typical centre engine, showing some further details which may not be readily apparent in the previous illustrations. Altogether about 265 of these little centre engines with duplex cylinders were made over the period 1870–1934.

Swings, at first operated by the energy of the swinger, were common on English fairgrounds many years before the application of steam power. But when steam was first applied to what we may call the Human Pendulum, the swinger (or victim, depending upon the

Fig 301 Alternative type of centre engine.

Fig 302 General arrangement drawing of the Savage duplex centre engine.

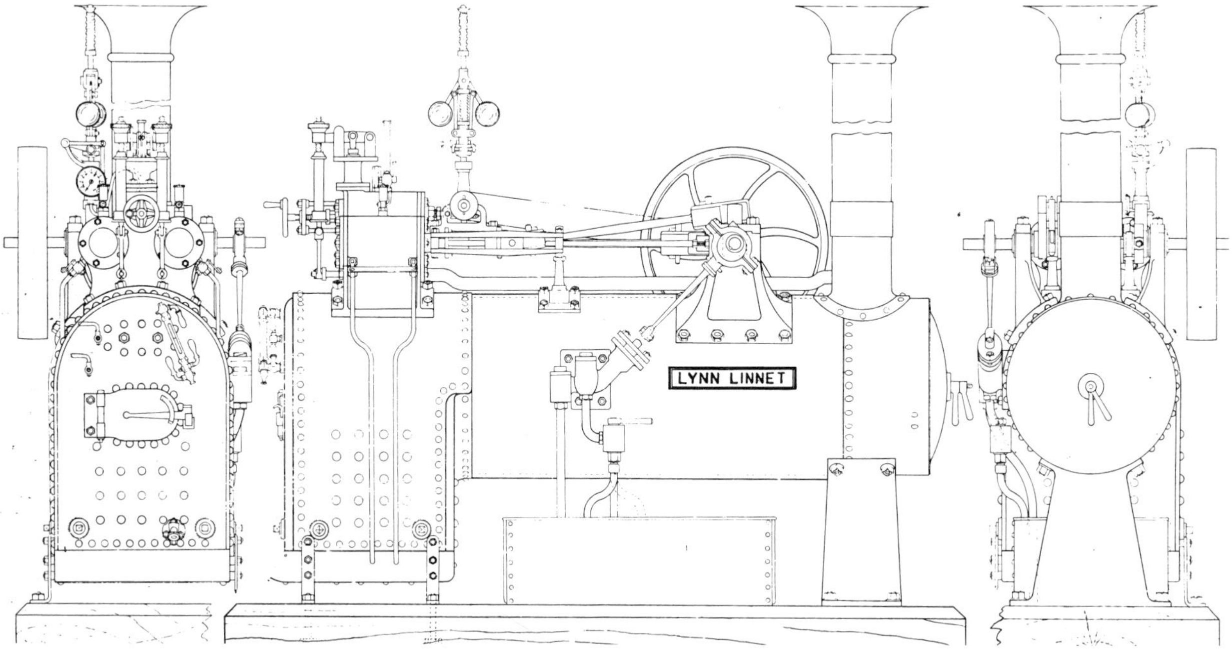

LYNN LINNET

Fig 303 View on the famous Savage steam swings.

reader's point of view!) was seated in a shallow box recalling a crude form of boat delineated in Fig 303. It was not long before the public dubbed them steam boats, swings or yachts. The drive to the overhead shafts carrying the two swings was by a pitch chain round sprockets on each end of the crankshaft and on the overhead shafts as in Fig 303. To drive these required a more powerful engine than the smaller centre type and an imperative condition was that the crankshaft must not rotate – the cranks must only reciprocate a little short of the inner and outer dead centres. Otherwise the result is easily imagined!

The two bigger cylinders 10½in x 16in were mounted on a larger locomotive type boiler but there was no flywheel and no familiar valve gear. Although the cylinders were both fitted with slide valves their operation was by a special valve gear illustrated in Fig 304, where a pin N projecting from the crosshead strikes the ends M of the gear which is free to oscillate as struck with the pivot P. This oscillation causes the lever R to describe a small arc culminating in a reciprocating motion being given to the slide valve. A hand or gab lever V is fitted to the side of the firebox so that the slide valve can be hand operated for starting up after which the action becomes automatic, when it is curious to watch the lever V moving to and fro untouched by

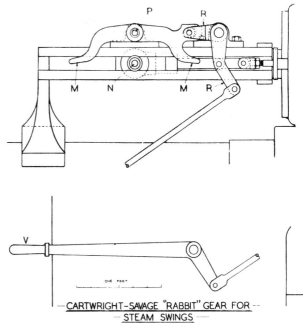

CARTWRIGHT-SAVAGE "RABBIT" GEAR FOR STEAM SWINGS

Fig 304 Valve or Rabbit Gear for the steam swings.

hand. This trip gear and layout of the complete unit was the subject of Patent No 15138 of 1894 in the name of William Cartwright, of West Bromwich, "Mechanical Engineer", and as it was taken up and adopted by Savage it became known as "Savage's" gear as Howe's

193

reversing gear upon being used by Stephenson became known as "Stephenson's" gear. There had been a previous patent No 9375 of 1888, relating to these swing boats where only one boat was used, with the engine at one side but having the cylinder and gear vertical. This was in the names of William Cartwright, as in the previous case, but allied with one Henry Cracknell, also of West Bromwich, "musician". Colloquially this mechanism was also referred to as the "Rabbit Gear" owing to its configuration resembling an outline of that familiar animal.

Another popular fairground machine was the Tunnel Railway where coaches were hauled around a circular track usually of 40 feet diameter, by a diminutive 2-2-2 locomotive arranged with a permanent inside "list", apparent in Fig 305. It was quite an unusual application for a steam locomotive and the attraction for the riders was the dark tunnel for half of the circumference of the ride, especially esteemed by the lovelorn! Usually the gauge was three feet and the engine cylinders 4½in x 7in. An outline drawing is included in Fig 306. Approximately half a dozen were made in 1895/6. At this time there was one of those periodic preambles towards a Channel Tunnel so this type of amusement was then quite topical.

It was long the custom for fairground attractions and

rides to operate accompanied by the latest "pop" musical hits of the day and many were the makes of organs applied to, and part of, the roundabout or similar machine. These organs were air-operated and to drive the instrument, which included working the bellows or barrels, a small neat vertical single cylinder engine of about 1 nhp was designed to do this work. We shall see later (under S. G. Soame) how the organ engine evolved. In course of time Savage made his own and literally dozens left St. Nicholas Works. Two typical organ engines are shown in Fig 307 each having a cylinder 3in x 4in although in some cases the earlier engines had a bore of only 2½in. They were beautifully finished and painted and were pretty little engines to watch at work. Some showmen referred to them as the "model".

Not every showman had a road locomotive to haul his tackle and complete with dynamo to provide his lighting therefore Frederick Savage produced what was called the "electric light" engine. In reality it was adapted from the firm's later portable engines but with the cylinder mounted at the chimney end of the boiler and with the crankshaft over the firebox end to give long belt centres to the dynamo placed on the platform just in front of the smokebox, all clearly seen in Fig 308. When in use, the extension chimney was placed through a hole in the canopy and into the chimney base to receive it on the smokebox. The whole unit was

Fig 305 View of a Tunnel Railway Locomotive.

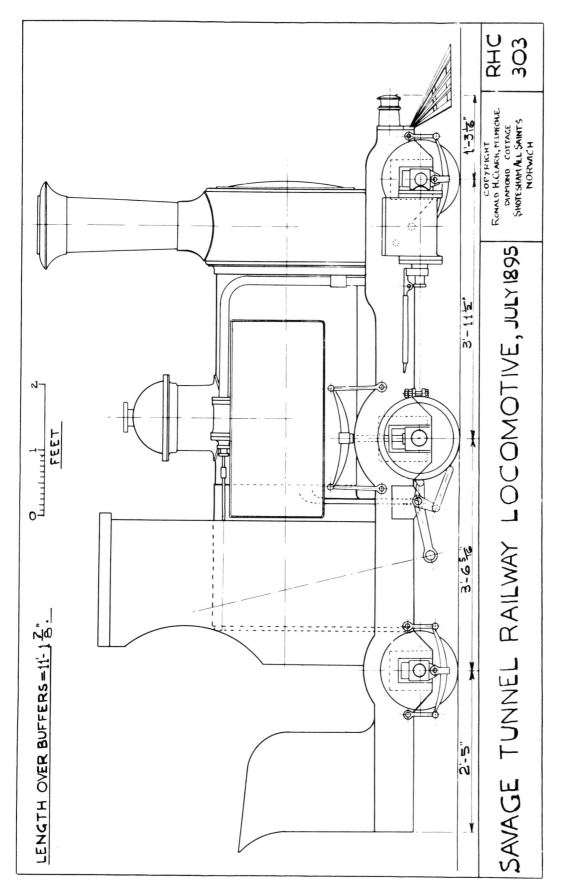

LENGTH OVER BUFFERS = 11'-1⅞".

FEET

SAVAGE TUNNEL RAILWAY LOCOMOTIVE, JULY 1895

COPYRIGHT
RONALD H.CLARK, M.I.MECH.E.
DIAMOND COTTAGE
SHOTESHAM ALL SAINTS
NORWICH

RHC
303

Fig 306 Further details of the Tunnel Railway Locomotive.

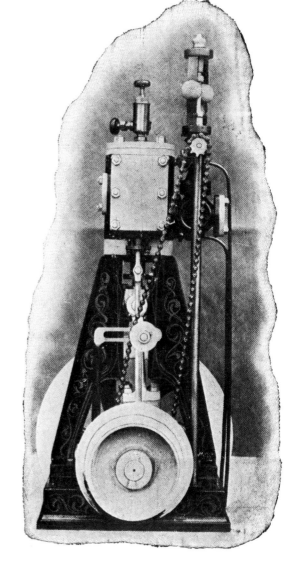

Fig 307 Savage's organ engine, in two forms.

mounted on four road wheels and with shafts for horse traction, when required. Made with both single and compound cylinders the single had a bore and stroke of 6¾in x 9in, the compounds being rated at 4, 6 and 8 nhp, the last having cylinders 6½in and 11in x 12in. At least one 4 nhp electric light engine with a single cylinder is preserved in private possession. As will be noted in Fig 308, the upper parts of the machine could be closed in by the surrounding wooden sides and the lot securely locked, and these sides were decorated in contrasting showground colours.

Frederick Savage and his successors were no exception to the general rule that all good engineers should fix a good nameplate and in Fig 309 we have probably a complete selection of Savage nameplates

fitted to various engines over the many years they were manufacturers.

1 The earliest is this heart-shaped design fitted to engine No 30 and dated 1862. It was an interesting engine having been built as a 7 nhp portable but was converted later to a chain-driven traction engine which finally finished its working life in central Norfolk. Size 13in x 7½in x 1⅛in wide.

2 The traction engines wore two plates, this example in brass being fitted to the valve chest cover. Size 8in x 6½in. *PAGE 198*

3 The other traction engine plate of cast iron was fitted to the lower curve of the cylinder block, on the right-hand side. It is an excellent example of fine iron casting, the details of the contemporary Royal Arms being sharply defined. Size 10¾in x 8in. *PAGE 198*

Fig 308 The Savage electric light engine complete with truck.

①

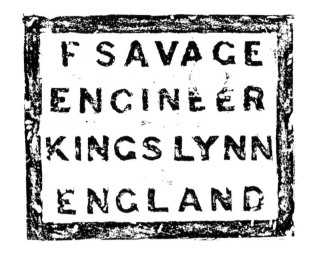

②

③

④

4 Of unusual shape in brass, this design was fixed to the roundabout centre engines of the right-hand crankshaft bracket, just below the bearing, and it is slotted to clear it. Size 12in wide x 12½in deep.

5 An hydraulic test plate in brass and fitted to the boiler backhead recording the test pressure of 150 psi for a working pressure of only 80 psi. Size 4in x 2½in.

6 An example of the Savage Brothers later style of nameplate, this plate being fitted to all the various classes of steam wagon. In brass size 11in x 7¼in.

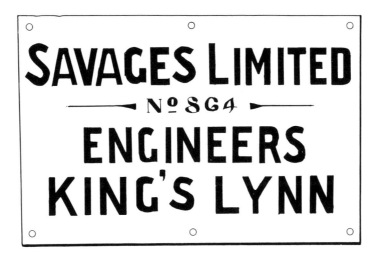

7 A Savages Limited engine plate as fitted to the later road engines, in this case to the last traction engine made, No 864, and completed in 1912. Size 11½in x 7½in. All are in the author's collection.

In Fig 310 is shown a very early advertising poster published by Frederick Savage when sole proprietor, together with a coloured poster on stiff card that was sent to prospective customers. It would grace any Victorian office wall and I hope aided some recipients in making up their minds what machinery to buy. Also shown are some letter headings, now of historic interest.

To my knowledge there remains no letter or other epistle in Frederick's Savage's own handwriting but fortunately his signature has survived and is illustrated in Fig 311. Appropriately, it is shown beneath his portrait which hitherto I think has been unpublished. A maker's signature is something usually omitted in steam engine literature so here I make amends.

Class	No. Off	CUSTOMER	Date
O	1	Ham Baker	
O	1	Morris Aiming Tube Co., London	
OA	1	Leicester Corporation. Sanitary wagon.	
OA	1	Cape Marine, S. Africa. 3-4 ton.	5/10/96
OA	1	Frost & Evans, Johannesburg.	
OA	1	A. & F. Bird, Millers. Lynn.	
OA	1	Marshall & Co., Driffield.	
OA	1	S. Wales Haulage Co.	
OA	1	Chivers, Histon.	
OA	1	Birds of Radstock.	
A	1	Marshall & Co.	1/11/06
A	1	Adnam's Brewery, Southwold.	8/11/06
A	1	Folkestone Corporation. 3-4 ton.	8/11/06
A	1	Portsmouth Corporation.	
A	1	G. Wray, Southport & Birkenhead.	
A	1	Stanfield & Co., Fulham.	
A	1	G. Thurston, Lowestoft. With ice body.	
A	1	to Buenos Aires, Argentine.	
A	1	Advance Wood Working Co., Newcastle Upon Tyne.	

(continued on page 203)

Fig 310 (facing page) Enterprise in early advertising, a Savage poster. Above: The famous erecting shop at St. Nicholas Works.

F. SAVAGE,

ENGINEER,

Portable Engine.

Combined Thrashing Machine.

SAINT NICHOLAS IRON WORKS,

Traction Engine.

Combined Thrashing Machine.

KINGS LYNN, NORFOLK.

AGENT FOR

PATENT MACHINES

AND

AGRICULTURAL IMPLEMENTS,

All selected from the best Makers, always kept in Stock, and

SOLD AT MAKERS' PRICES.

Trew and Son, Steam Machine Printers, High Street and Saturday Market, King's Lynn.

Fig 311 Portrait of Savage the Founder and his signature. Top left: Cast iron plaque showing
F. Savage on his No. 1 road engine.

A	1	Kensington Corporation.	13/7/05
A1	2	to Chili.	
B	1	Samuel Field, Showman, Ireland.	/04
B	1	Durham Corporation. ⅝ ton. Sanitary Wagon (on trial or return).	
B	1	to Australia.	/04
B	1	Birmingham Corporation. 5-6 ton. Sanitary Wagon (on trial or return).	
C	1	to Rome.	
C	1	to Spain.	
C	1	Cook & Co., London.	
C	1	to New Zealand.	
C	1	to Barbardos.	22/4/08
C	1	Customer not now known.	

Note – No complete list of wagons was ever found at the works and the above are compiled from researches into drawings, files and other notes. It may be there are one, or not more than two wagons, unaccounted for.

⚒ XXXIV ⚒

THOMAS SMITHDALE & SONS,
The Foundary, ACLE.

Originally established in 1847 by Thomas Smithdale, with premises known as St. Anne's Ironworks, just off King Street, Norwich, formerly occupied by Francis Buttifont & Son. In 1883 new works had been built at Panxworth but in 1897 another move took place to the Foundry, in Acle. Incidentally, the old Panxworth works still stands. Shortly after the move to Acle occurred, the Founder was joined by his son Arthur, who carried on the business until the approach of World War 2, after which several of his six sons were responsible for its continuance. However, the demand for repairs to steam engines, windmills and the installation of new pumping stations began to fall off and so did the business decline such that trading virtually finished in 1973/4, followed by an auction of all the plant and effects on 17th April 1974. The building and site were sold for £10,400. Incidentally, a small branch works had been started in 1900 in Ramsey St. Mary, Huntingdonshire, to deal with the then extensive local business in that area Thomas Smithdale had developed in millwrighting in connection with Fen drainage.

One most interesting engine produced just before the move to Acle was the 90° vee twin illustrated by the original woodcut in Fig 312. The cylinders were about

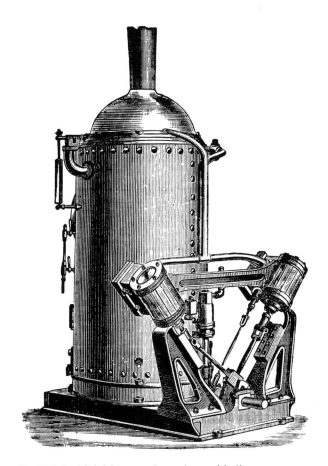

Fig 312 Smithdale's vee twin engine and boiler.

4in x 6in and with the cylinders at 90° the engine would start with the crank in any position. This design was non-reversing for stationary works, as will be seen. A vee twin engine fits neatly athwartwise in a boat or small vessel and where this was the case, Stephenson's gear was fitted. For land use the accompanying vertical boiler may be seen in Fig 312. For marine work it usually took the form of a small horizontal multi-tubular type.

In place of the vee twin in Fig 312 for land or agricultural work the customer could have a neat vertical engine and boiler shown in Fig 313. The cylinder 4in x 6in or 5in x 8in was mounted on two bent cast iron standards, the upper halves of which take the mounting for the crosshead guides. A jet condenser was driven by a lever worked off the eccentric rod. The flywheel was overhung and the cylinder was lagged with the polished strip mahogany typical at this period.

Another distinctive design of vertical engine was evolved in Norwich and made in Panxworth having only one curved upright or standard to support the cylinder. The standard was curved, making the engine appear to have a familiar deformity. In fact this type was always called colloquially in the works and by the

users as the "humpback vertical". The single cylinder
was 10in x 14in with the slide valve actuated by one
eccentric fitted outside the crankshaft bearing. Another
eccentric for working the feed pump was keyed to the
end of the crankshaft. A view of the lower portions of
one of these curious engines made from an old and
faded negative is shown in Fig 314. One of this design
drove a scoop wheel by double reduction gearing in a
small pumping station at Stokesby but it has now been
destroyed. The scoop wheel was sixteen feet diameter,
and the gear ratio of engine to wheel was 13½ : 1.

Like many other competitors Thomas Smithdale did
not neglect the horizontal engine and one example
produced at first in Norwich and later at Panxworth
and Acle is included in Fig 315. When condensing, the
jet condenser was in tandem behind the cylinder. No

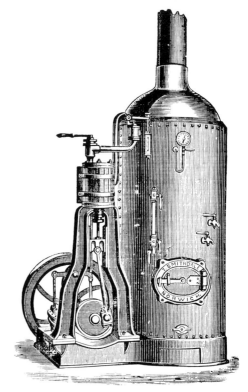

*Fig 313 (right) Vertical engine and boiler by
Thomas Smithdale.*

Fig 314 Smithdale's curious Humpback vertical engine.

Fig 315 Horizontal Smithdale engine with tandem condenser.

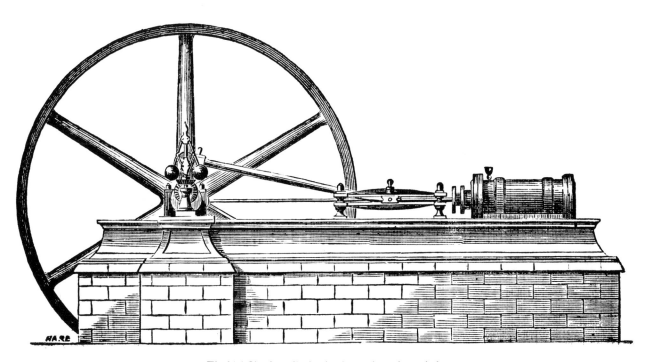

Fig 316 Single cylinder horizontal made at Acle.

tables of dimensions appear to have been published by the makers but the late Arthur Smithdale told me they were usually made to order and to suit the buyer's specification.

A simpler non-condensing horizontal engine is illustrated in Fig 316 with unlagged cylinder, single eccentric and large flywheel. Such a simple design, cheap to produce, was aimed at the agricultural community who wanted a straightforward engine which was reliable for driving barn machinery and so on.

There was a more elaborate and larger horizontal of which some of the major details are depicted in Fig 317. Here the cylinder was 13in x 20in, neatly lagged, a crankshaft 5in diameter carrying a flywheel ten feet diameter. The unloaded Watt-type governor was of an elegant design on a finely proportioned fluted cast iron column, enhancing the general appearance of the whole engine. This governor controlled an expansion valve on the outside of the main valve thus governing by expansion of the steam. Fortunately, this engine bore the date 1867 which means it was made when Thomas Smithdale was active in Norwich. It worked for many years in a pumping station in South Walsham, driving a vertical spindle turbine pump, but was destroyed many years ago.

As we have seen, the vee twin engine in Fig 312 could be adapted for fitting in a small vessel, but

Fig 317 A larger Smithdale horizontal pumping engine.

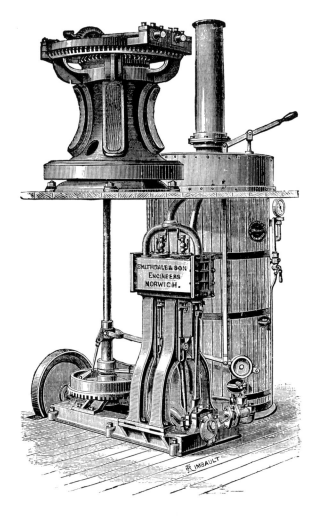

Fig 318 Smithdale's marine steam capstan.

another Smithdale venture into marine work was the compact capstan, engine and vertical boiler shown in Fig 318. As the nameplate shows, it was evolved in the Norwich works, the engine being a vertical with duplex cylinders about 4in x 8in with slide valves on the outside and therefore very accessible. The rather squat vertical boiler was heavily lagged with polished pine in this case and with the feed pump eccentric driven off the end of the crankshaft. The remaining details of the unit are quite clear from the engraving.

There remains one other most interesting Smithdale production, viz. the inclined winch with 4½ x 6in duplex cylinders, illustrated in Fig 319. Both winch and vertical unlagged boiler were mounted on four cast iron wheels for portability and trunk crosshead guides were favoured in this case. The countershaft was driven by two reduction pinions on the end of the crankshaft behind the boiler and from a pulley on this shaft ran a flat belt, seen on the left-hand end, driving another countershaft across the sheer-legs, and then by another pair of pinions the rope drum. This double reduction gearing enabled the relatively small cylinders to raise the heavy monkey necessary to drive the various well-

boring tools. The well seen at this site was finally driven 207 feet deep with the water settling at 112 feet.

When the owners, W. & G. Fake, retired from business, the author was instrumental in this locally-made and unusual engine being given to the City of Norwich as an example of local industry and it was taken temporarily to the Castle Keep. Curiously it is not now to be found!

✦ XXXV ✦

S. G. SOAME,
Perseverance Works, MARSHAM.

The founder, Sidney George Soame, was born in the 1840s and had established his small works, probably on the site of an earlier smithy, by 1860, alongside the main road. In 1896 Soame purchased the leasehold of the works and the adjoining land. His son, George Sidney

ARTESIAN WELL,
(207 feet deep, Water 112 feet from Surface,)
At Home Farm, Upper Sheringham, for H. M. UPCHER, Esq.,
BY
W. & G. FAKE, Artesian Well Engineers, Tube Well Drivers,
Well Sinkers and Pump Makers, NORWICH.

(See "On The Trail.")

Fig 319 A rare engine, Thomas Smithdale's inclined steam winch.

Fig 320 First roundabout engine of all time by S. G. Soame.

Soame, was born in 1875 and along with his uncle Thomas, joined the business. In 1904 this son George set up Soames's Motor Car Works adjacent to the carpenter's shop of the main works. It was probably one of the first real motor garages and works to be opened in the county. Both the garage and engineering works were amalgamated by G. S. Soame c1920 when he advertised that *"Motor cars, steam wagons and petrol lorries sold and repaired; engineer, boiler maker, general machinist and iron and brass founder, steam engines, threshing machines and all kinds of agricultural implements made and repaired"*. Note that steam engines were included in what could be made. It is also interesting to recall that at this period petrol was sold in two-gallon cans with the stoppers sealed. Each can carried the notice, *"Refuse this can if the seal be broken"*. S. G. Soame the Founder died in 1917 and his son George died on 21st February 1937, aged 62, after which his son Frederick Soame, aided by their Work's

Manager Mr. C. A. Cushion, carried on the works until the end of 1940 when it was sold to Kent Brothers. In 1947 the Eastern Counties Farmer's Co. acquired the site and premises, when the old works became their machine shops and dépôt. The family had lived in the Foundry House built in the 1840s, adjacent to the works on the Norwich side. The workforce in the 1890s averaged sixteen though at times it reached thirty. In plan the works were L-shaped, with the erecting and machine shop at right angles to the main road. The smith's shop, foundry and fettling shop formed the longer side of the L and were parallel to the main road. For some years up to World War 2 the machinery was driven by a small semi-portable by Robert Tidman of Norwich (see No XXXVIII).

Sidney G. Soame should be remembered as the maker of the first steam roundabout engine in the country in c1864. As his son George mentioned to me, this first engine was made for Samuel High of Blofield,

Norfolk, and it was shown working primitive merry-go-rounds, first at Aylsham and then at fairs in Norwich and Lynn, in 1864/5. As far as he could recollect, his father made three such engines and an old photograph reproduced in Fig 320 shows the maker standing adjacent to the boiler backhead. A belt from the flywheel transmitted the power to the inlet pulley on the roundabout. The small duplex cylinders were 3½in x 6in. Two interesting details are the lagging of strip hardwood, polished and extended to lag the smokebox, and the artistically curved spokes in the flywheel. Curved spokes were less likely to fracture as the casting cooled in the sand than if they were straight.

To obviate the hand-turning of the organ accompanying the merry-go-round, Soame designed a small vertical engine on purpose to drive these little organs and again he was the first to produce what became known as the "organ engine". Fig 321, a posed photograph, shows the proud maker regarding his first organ engine. Only one size was made and a view on the valve chest side of what was one of the first half dozen or so is included in Fig 322. This little engine is a treasured possession in the author's collection and the single cylinder is 2in x 2¾in.

Fig 321 First organ engine of all time, also by S. G. Soame.

Fig 322 Another view of Soame's little organ engine.

Frederick Savage (No XXXIII), who was born in the next village of Hevingham, inspected Soames's engines at Aylsham Fair and later developed these two classes of engine with the result we have observed previously.

Several small portables were also produced at Marsham but unfortunately no illustration of one of them has turned up. However, Frederick Soame told me they had one back for repairs as late as October-December 1914.

One or more robust single cylinder vertical engines left the works for various customers and one went to Norwich laundry where it worked successfully until 1942, when it was scrapped. However I was able to secure the 8in x 10in cylinder for preservation in the Bridewell Museum, Norwich, and it is shown in Fig 323. The intention was that it would illustrate to students the arrangement of steam and exhaust ports in an ordinary engine but sad to relate, it is not now on display.

One Soame product is, however, preserved complete and in working order and is now the famous steam cart shown in Fig 324. In the safe possession of William McAlpine, it has cross-coupled compound cylinders 2¾in and 4½in x 6in, using steam from a renovated vertical boiler at 135 psi. Completed by Sidney G. Soame in 1897, it was later given the registration number AH 136. As will be seen, the final drive was by a flat belt 4in wide, which was prone to slip in wet weather. Under good conditions it would touch 25 mph but being then a little uncomfortable, it was usually cruised at 15 mph. Besides the iron-tyred wheels it has a full length canopy and tiller control with Ackerman type steering. Mr Soame made many trips to Norwich, Foulsham and North Norfolk and when in Norwich it was "stabled" in the White Horse Inn yard at Magdalen Street. He used it less frequently after 1905, however, after which it was stored in a lean-to shed at the works

Fig 324 The famous Steam Cart made at Marsham.

Fig 325 Boring a cylinder at the Marsham Works.

until it was sold privately in 1946. As the gears were arranged similarly to those on a traction engine, the cart had to be stopped for gear changing. Usually Mr. Soame had a mate to steer for him.

With the exception of the McKenzie Brougham (see No XXV) and the omnibus by Charles Burrell, this Soame passenger vehicle was the only other such made in the county, the cart being made completely at Marsham.

A good indication of how versatile and full of jobs the works were at one time the unusual picture in Fig 325 shows, a client's roller having the cylinder rebored where the belt drive to the boring bar from a small paraffin engine intruded over the footpath. No one objected; it was helping local employment and on wintry days as I can testify, the rural policeman sought warmth and shelter for a few minutes against one of the forges.

A fitting conclusion is the Soame nameplate illustrated in Fig 326 together with a letter heading. This little plate 5in x 3in is interesting being a palimpsest. On the reverse are the letters Me in flowing script, being part of the inscription on a memorial brass c1780 commencing "In Loving Memory . . . .".

Fig 326 A palimpsest nameplate of Soame and a letter heading (over page).

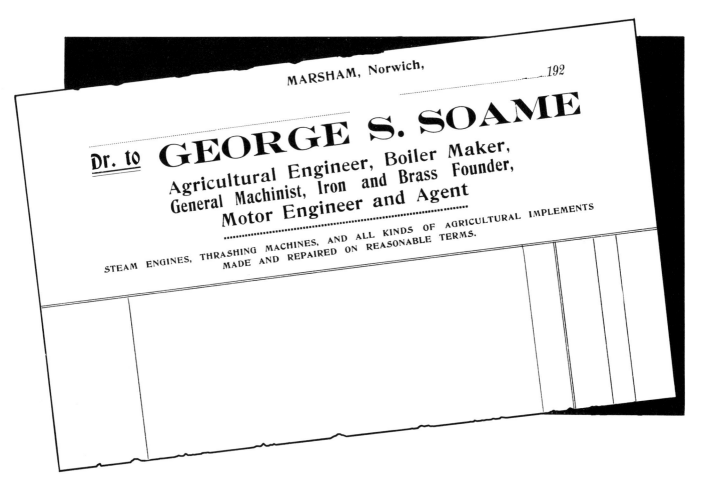

XXXVI

SPARKE & CO.,
Thorne Lane Foundry, NORWICH.

First mention of this firm appers in 1845 when they were described as "General engineers and Iron and Brass Founders and Agricultural Implement Makers", their address being Thorne Lane Foundry with Alfred Sparke the proprietor. By 1865 they had additional offices and show rooms on Castle Hill. Apparently the site of the Foundry was not far from the church of St. Michael at Thorne, which was destroyed by enemy action in 1941. When the firm finally closed down is not now certain.

Their chief engines manufactured appear to be portables and of these two types were made. The first and smaller was a standard little machine of only 3 nhp, carried on four cast iron road wheels and with the cylinder close to the chimney. The makers claimed that steam could be raised in thirty minutes and the engine could be *"worked by any intelligent labourer without liability of getting out of repair"*. The cylinder was about 4¾in x 9in. Another claim by Sparke & Co. was that this engine will work for ten hours for two hundredweights of coals. An example of this little unit

is illustrated in Fig 327 which was unusual in as much that it had a cylindrical firebox fired from above the rear water space, the smoke tubes leading to the smokebox in the normal way. However, the horse shafts were fitted at the firebox or rear end which was most uncommon. With the boiler felted and lagged and on the four cast iron wheels the list price was only £90. If the buyer preferred standard-type wood road wheels these would cost £5 extra.

Another and quite imposing portable design is depicted in Fig 328 illustrating the 6 nhp engine, the range covering 5, 6, 7, 8 and 10 nhp with a single cylinder and 12 and 14 nhp with duplex cylinders. Boiler plates were of best Staffordshire, and fireboxes of Lowmoor Iron. Curiously, the test pressure is quoted as 100 psi so presumably in 1865 the working pressure would be about 75 psi. The 5 nhp was priced at £180, the 6 nhp illustrated at £200 and the 14 nhp with duplex cylinders cost £360. The cylinder, it will be noted, was built into the top of the smokebox and therefore kept heated by the flue gases. However, if the

Fig 327 Sparke & Co's. small portable engine.

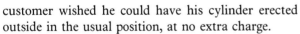

Fig 329 Horizontal engine also by Sparke & Co.

Fig 328 Large portable by Sparke & Co.

customer wished he could have his cylinder erected outside in the usual position, at no extra charge.

In Fig 329 we have illustrated Sparke & Co's compact little 3 nhp horizontal engine. The cylinder and motion are erected on an open-type cast iron bedplate, the whole mounted on brickwork or stone foundation of a height to suit the conditions on site. One interesting feature was the position of the slide valve – on top of the cylinder instead of at the side and actuated by a small rocker shaft receiving its motion from the eccentric rod in the normal way.

Thorne Lane Foundry could supply another type of engine illustrated in Fig 330 from an old engraving. Of

the crank-overhead type the crankshaft rotated in two bearings, each on its own A frame, both frames being mounted on a stout cast iron bedplate. In this arrangement the cylinder was below floor level, in a room or basement, and suspended from the bedplate. The overhead crank was overhung as shown, with the flywheel inside and close to the bearing. On the far end, outside the bearing, was the pulley for belt drive. With curved spokes and tapering legs of the A frames it was a picturesque-looking engine. The makers in their catalogue said "*The principles of these engines is direct acting, thereby simplifying the working parts and rendering them less likely to get out of repair*".

Fig 330 Sparke & Co's. elegant crank-overhead engine.

Unfortunately no records of cylinder sizes and main dimensions appear to exist but they were supplied with a Cornish boiler complete with all fittings. The smallest was rated at 4 nhp and the range covered nine sizes rising by 2 nhp to a maximum of twenty. The 4 nhp cost £120, the 12 nhp £300 and the 20 nhp £420 inclusive of the boiler and the fixing in position. It did not include carriage, masonry or brickwork.

⮑ XXXVII ⮐

STURGESS & TOWLSON,
Vulcan Ironworks, Oak Street, NORWICH.

The exact date when this firm commenced business is not now known but John Towlson was described as an Engineer Mechanical by 1869, and later in 1888 the partnership were styled Iron & Brass Founders, Millwrights, Hydraulic Machinery Engineers and Makers of all Classes of Steam Engines from 2 to 60 nhp. When Sturgess joined Towlson is not certain. In

their later days Towlson had dropped out, the title then becoming Sturgess & Harvey, until they finally retired from business, the foundry then being acquired by G. E. Hawes & Son who specialised in castings for school desks and allied furniture.

During their active period Sturgess & Towlson were responsible for several fine horizontal engines made for Norwich concerns. For example, a large horizontal of 60 nhp was built and installed in Francis Hinde's silk and crêpe mills in the city. Having compound cylinders, the governor controlled the travel of the expansion valve reciprocating on the back of the main slide valve, thus providing a practically constant crankshaft speed so important when driving textile machinery. It is regretted that no further details or illustration of such a fine engine have turned up.

Fig 331 A rarity, the Sturgess & Towlson vee twin launch engine.

Besides horizontal and vertical engines they made a very interesting vee twin marine engine, fortunately now preserved in the Bridewell Museum, Norwich, and seen in Fig 331. For many years it powered a steam launch well known on the Broads called the *Vivid*. The cylinders 4¼in x 6in are set at 90° and as we have seen, such an arrangement allows the engine to start with the crank in any position. Stephenson's link motion is fitted to each cylinder and the ingenuity lies in how the gear operates with only two eccentrics but which will be more easily understood from the general arrangement drawing included in Fig 332. The date of the *Vivid* was 1875. When the launch, registered at Horstead incidentally, was broken up just after World War 1, the writer's father, the late H. O. Clark, begged the engine lying rusting in the open at Wroxham from Mr. A. Thrower, the boatyard owner. It was then presented to

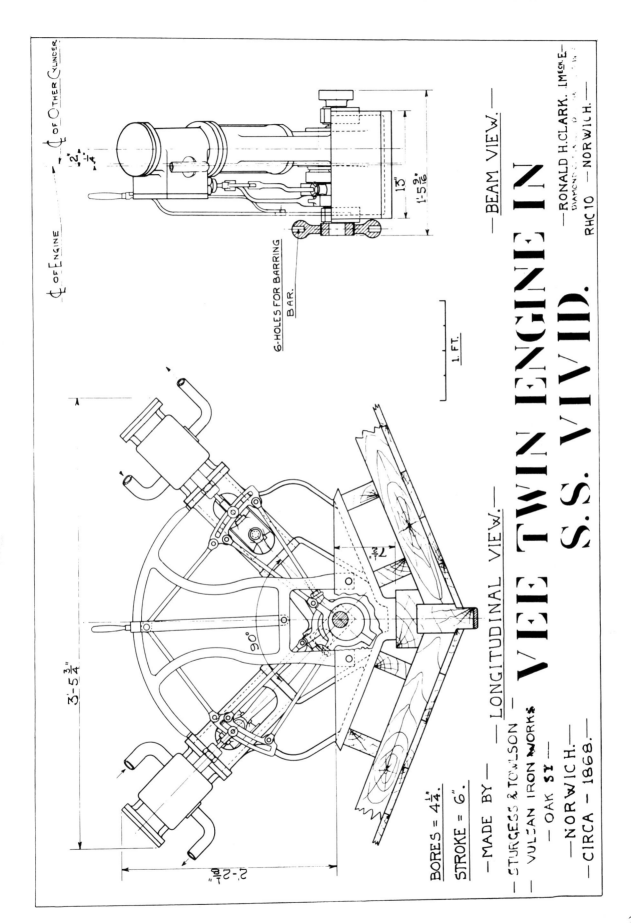

CENTRE OF OTHER CYLINDER

CENTRE OF ENGINE

2'¼"

15"

1'-5 9/16"

6-HOLES FOR BARRING BAR.

— BEAM VIEW. —

— RONALD H.CLARK. I.MECH.E—
DIAMOND
RHC 10 — NORWICH.

1 FT.

3'-5¾"

90°

2"

2'-2⅛"

BORES = 4¼".
STROKE = 6".

— MADE BY —

— STURGESS & TOWLSON —
— VULCAN IRON WORKS —
— OAK ST —
— NORWICH. —
— CIRCA — 1868. —

— LONGITUDINAL VIEW. —

VEE TWIN ENGINE IN
S.S. VIVID.

Fig 332 General arrangement drawing of the vee twin in Fig 331.

215

Fig 333 How Sturgess & Towlson cast their name.

the Bridewell Museum, Norwich, in which my father was very interested and had a hand in helping to start it as a Museum of Local Industry. After once being lost and several other vicissitudes it was overhauled by a country engineering firm in Shotesham All Saints and is now on display. A similar engine was made for and installed in a 47ft 5in launch named *Emma Jeannie*.

Sturgess & Towlson produced most excellent castings and railings on Trowse Bridge and those round the churchyard of St. Peter Parmentergate in Norwich were cast by them. Many bear their name cast in relief in sharp capitals as one can see from Fig 333.

One of their small verticals made in 1884 drove a Paris & Scott generator providing electric lighting in another steam launch believed to be similar to the *Emma Jeannie* previously mentioned. Apparently they later produced castings only for Paris & Scott who were then constructing a peripatetic dynamo for the Carrow Works of J. & J. Colman.

⟡ XXXVIII ⟡

ROBERT TIDMAN & SONS,
Bishop Bridge Iron Works, NORWICH.

At some date in 1847 Robert Tidman of Norwich, having learned the trade of a boiler-maker and blacksmith, unfortunately it is not known where or with whom, was so successful in carrying out repairs to the plant in the watermill at Stoke Holy Cross, five miles south of Norwich, that he deemed it opportune to commence on his own account in small premises at the lower end of Rosary Road in this city and adjacent to Bishop Bridge. Much of his early work covered the installation of small boilers and general millwrighting. As a commentary on individual enterprise at that time – Robert the Founder walked to Stoke in the morning and back in the evening with his tools on his back, there being no other transport available.

It may not be generally known that at this period Stoke Holy Cross mill, the lowest of three on the River Tas, was owned and used by Jeremiah James Colman who later erected premises at Carrow, then on the outskirts of Norwich. J. J. Colman needs no introduction as the famous mustard manufacturer and today's mustard and other comestibles are still produced at Carrow Works.

After a few years Tidman's premises comprised blacksmith, boiler-maker's and engineer's shops, constituting what had now become known as Bishop Bridge Iron Works. In 1883 Robert was joined by his two sons, Robert and Frederick, who as a trio, carried on the business until their father's death, after which it was continued by them with the help of Frederick's son, also called Robert. At this time too they opened an office nearby at 3 Rosary Road. The actual site of the works lay between the "King's Arms" and the "Evening Gun" public houses. The former still stands.

Before the foundry was in operation the Tidman Brothers undertook to erect the new or third bridge close to Thorpe Station, Norwich, known because of LeFevre's Foundry close by on the other bank of the River Wensum, as Foundry Bridge. For this structure the main compound girders were supplied by a Yorkshire firm and the parapet castings by Sabberton Brothers (see No XXXII). The tracing showing the design and method of erection of the bridge is dated 23rd December 1884 and an important note thereon stipulates that the bridge is to be erected in halves, the upstream half to be finished first. Not only was the erection entrusted to Tidmans but also the preliminary machining of the panels and sections, which were then temporarily built up in the works before being finally placed in position and bolted up on the permanent site. This bridge is still one of the most important in the City of Norwich.

Probably Robert Tidman & Sons became better known for their fairground machinery and for many years a machine of some sort was always in progress at Bishop Bridge Works. One of their earliest designs is shown in Fig 334 when it was just opening for business and set up on Castle Hill, Norwich. This particular machine, known as a set of three-abreast gallopers, had delightfully scenic and picturesque rounding boards bedecked overall by the canvas tilt coloured red and white as shown. The platform was the subject of Robert and Frederick's Patent No 6244 of 8th May 1886.

But it is with the steam part of their manufacture that is our interest here and a view of the Tidman centre

Fig 334 Typical Tidman roundabout set up on Castle Hill, Norwich.

Fig 335 Tidman's roundabout centre engine.

engine is included in Fig 335. In this form its position in the ride or roundabout would be as in Fig 334, i.e. on the left-hand side of the centre and with the attendant standing close by. The drive was by a small bevel on the end of the crankshaft meshing with a larger bevel wheel on the lower end of the upright pole forming the rotating centre of the ride. For this arrangement the exhaust steam and smoke were taken from below the smokebox and through a horizontal rectangular duct into the hollow centre pole acting also as a chimney, the extreme top being visible above the tilt in Fig 334. A study of Fig 335 will show what delightful looking engines they were, all parts properly proportioned and complete with feed pump, injector, spring-loaded Watt-type governor, siren and all other necessary fittings. All parts not painted were highly polished which, as Mr. Tidman once told me, was their "No 1 finish". Fire and smoke boxes were painted glossy black and the

boiler cladding any tint specified by the customer. After all necessary priming coats, four coats of main colour were applied, each rubbed down and finished with two of best carriage varnish. Note the name BRITANNIA formed by an oval transfer.

The most popular engine had cylinders 3¾in x 8in taking steam at 120 psi but as rides got larger and heavier after about 1900 or so, a larger version had the cylinders increased to 4½in x 8in working at the same pressure. There were slight differences between the two as will be seen from Fig 336 showing an example of the larger engine. To make this section on centre engines more complete there is included in Fig 337 a general arrangement drawing which may be studied as typical of the two versions. To give an idea of the proportions, the connecting rod centres are 2ft 3in, bellied at the centre and carefully designed.

Fig 336 The larger Tidman centre engine.

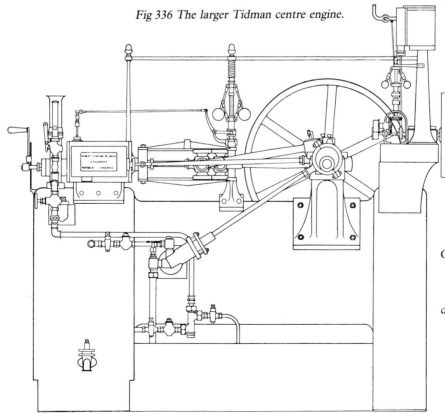

Fig 337
General arrangement
drawing
of the Tidman
duplex centre engine.

219

Besides the gallopers another favourite Tidman ride was their switchback where the vehicles take the form of motor cars of the period. A showman could have as an alternative Venetian Gondolas if he wished, and most ornately finished they were. In the design of a switchback the centre pole remains but the engine itself is mounted on a very robust four-wheeled truck and forms the anchored base of the pole as will be seen in the drawing in Fig 338. The drive to the cheese wheel at the top is by a vertical shaft bevel driven from the crankshaft, clearly shown in the drawing, the adjoining part of which shows the top section of the pole together with the top roller bearing to steady the spinning top gear. The machine is permitted to revolve at the centre pole by virtue of a set of heavy duty rollers in the top bearing to take lateral thrusts and loads, a set of thinner rollers just below carrying the downwards loading. Again the centre pole is hollow and its upper section is hinged at its lower end to the top of the centre engine chimney by a suitable pair of brackets and at the top carries another roller bearing to steady the spinning top gear. Ground level to the top of the pole was 23ft 10⅞in, the diameter over the swifts being 42 feet.

The vertical drive shaft bevel driven off the engine crankshaft, runs in a hemispherical footstep bearing and a plain journal bearing at the top held parallel to the centre pole by a suitable bracket. Vertical adjustment was by the screw and lever shown on the drawing.

Tidman's centre engine boiler was a fine design, excellently made, and the details to be found in Fig 339. The heating surface is made up of:-

Tubes	41·15 sq ft
Firebox	12·84 sq ft
Total	53·99 sq ft
Grate area	2·55 sq ft

In working, and like all small boilers, the pressure tended to vary unless the firing was done correctly and based on "a little and often" so the attendants became very skilled in this matter. Additionally, they could set the pump so that its rate of feed kept the water level constant. An excellent feature was the shell rolled from one plate and therefore with no riveted seams, its outside diameter being 1ft 9in, the overall length of the

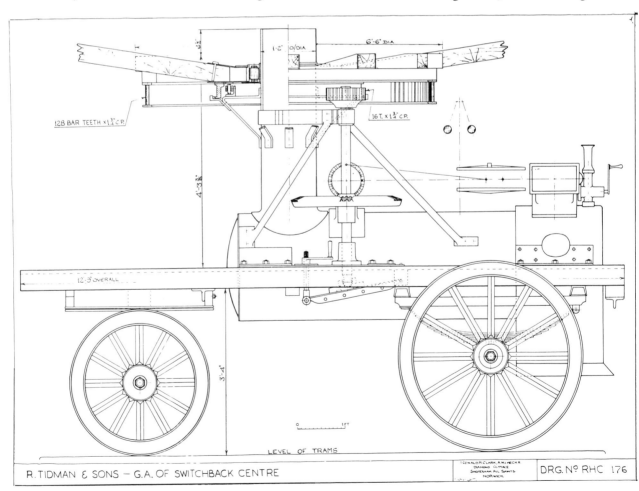

R. TIDMAN & SONS — G.A. OF SWITCHBACK CENTRE   DRG. No RHC 176

Fig 338 Centre engine mounted by R. Tidman on a road truck.

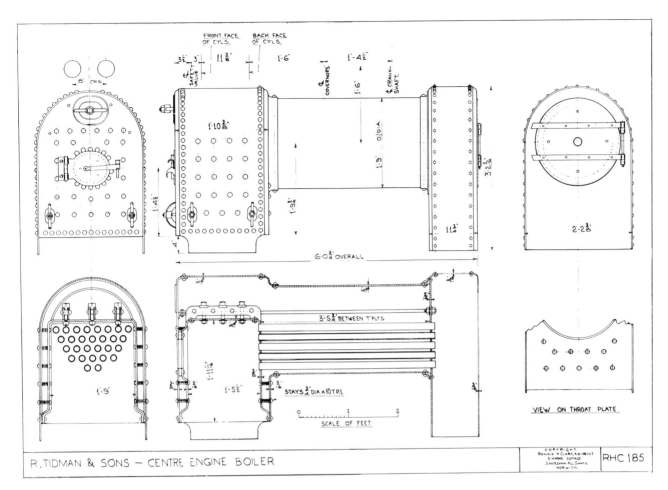

COPYRIGHT
RONALD H CLARK AMIMECHE
DIAMOND COTTAGE
SHOTESHAM ALL SAINTS
NORWICH.

RHC 185

R. TIDMAN & SONS – CENTRE ENGINE BOILER

VIEW ON THROAT PLATE

SCALE OF FEET

Fig 339 Drawing of a Tidman centre engine locomotive-type boiler.

complete boiler being 6ft 0¾in. There were 28 tubes and the length between tubeplates was 3ft 5¾in. Several boilers of this design were made for the Howcroft Engineering Company of West Hartlepool and another was supplied to Messrs. Gaymers Limited, the cider manufacturers of Attleborough, for process steam.

The centre engines were also supplied as an overtype for ordinary stationary purposes and that illustrated in Fig 340 has the typical portable engine form of smokebox instead of the downdraught design as when used with a roundabout. Fig 340 shows the clean exterior of the boiler which in this case was temporarily unlagged.

Another application by Tidmans of their centre engine took the form of a portable electric light engine shown in the drawing in Fig 341. These electric light engines gradually ousted the messy paraffin and naphtha flares used on the fairground and most showmen had one sort or another until the road locomotive with its front-mounted dynamo in turn superseded it. In Fig 341 the overall length and width of the platform was 14ft 1in x 6ft 0in and the height above ground level 4ft 7in. For the dynamos Tidman's went to

Fig 340 A Tidman centre engine modified as an overtype.

221

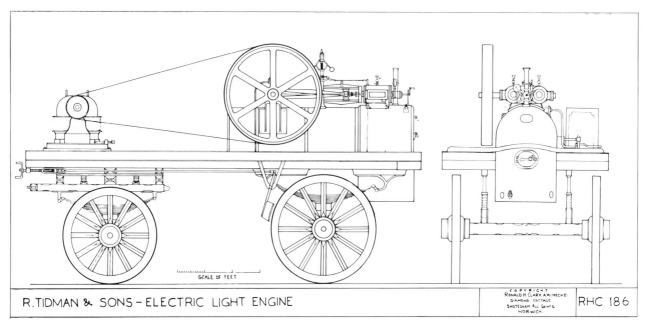

R.TIDMAN & SONS – ELECTRIC LIGHT ENGINE

COPYRIGHT
RONALD H CLARK A.M.I.MECH.E·
DIAMOND COTTAGE
SHOTESHAM ALL SAINTS
NORWICH.

RHC 186

Fig 341 The Tidman electric light engine and generator.

their neighbours Laurence, Scott & Co. Ltd. (No XXII) in the same city and the fine twin magnet machine seen in Fig 341 is typical of this period. Usually the voltage was 110 dc, the engine speed being controlled by a spring-loaded Watt-type governor. The whole outfit was painted and gilded in true showman's style, often with the boiler barrel in a bright glossy maroon.

Like other firms catering for the showmen's needs, Bishop Bridge Iron Works produced an elegant and compact organ engine and two different examples are shown in Figs 342 & 343. Note the different design of bases on the smokebox. The single cylinder was 3in x 4in. Alternatively, the customer could have one of these engines made horizontal and where no centre engine was involved, as for example a side show of some sort, it was supplied complete with small vertical boiler, the whole unit being illustrated by the photograph in Fig 342. Note only three spanners were required for any maintenance work. Should a customer desire an even smaller engine he could have one with a cylinder only 2in x 3½in and a flywheel of 12in diameter, the boiler being 1ft 5in outside diameter x 2 feet tall. It would be lagged with strip mahogany and highly polished and fixed by three equally-polished brass bands. If required, the unit could be mounted on a timber base, iron protected for engine and boiler, and with a small wheel at each corner for ease in manhandling on site.

A drawing showing a larger horizontal organ engine in plan and with a cylinder 3in x 4in is depicted in

Fig 342 Horizontal organ engine and boiler from the Bishop Bridge Works.

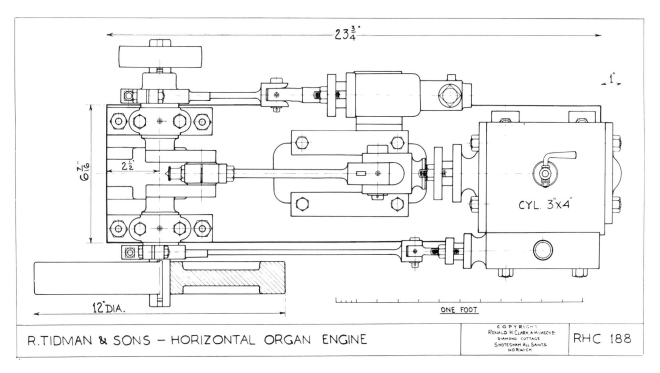

COPYRIGHT
RONALD H.CLARK A.M.I.MECH.E.
DIAMOND COTTAGE
SHOTESHAM ALL SAINTS
NORWICH

R.TIDMAN & SONS – HORIZONTAL ORGAN ENGINE   RHC 188

Fig 343 General arrangement drawing of the Tidman horizontal engine.

Fig 344 Drawing of a Tidman vertical organ engine.

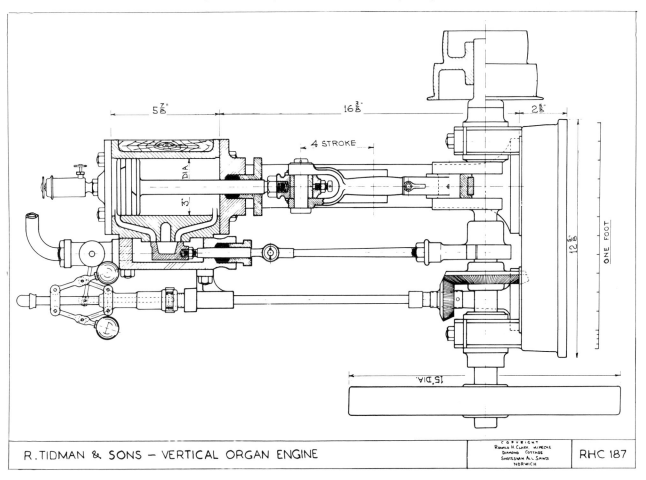

COPYRIGHT
RONALD H. CLARK. M.I.MECH.E
DIAMOND COTTAGE
SHOTESHAM ALL SAINTS
NORWICH

R.TIDMAN & SONS – VERTICAL ORGAN ENGINE   RHC 187

Fig 343. The belt drive to the organ could be from the crowned pulley on one end of the crankshaft or off the flywheel, and a small boiler feed pump was mounted between the pulley and the frame. One unit named *King Edward* was supplied to Messrs Pilkington Brothers of Warrington and there were many others made, both vertical and horizontal.

To complete this section on the organ engine there is illustrated in Fig 344 a general arrangement drawing of the vertical type prepared by the author from original torn and faded fragments and sketches. The 3in x 4in cylinder had unrestricted inlet ports and the governor placed near the steam pipe controlled the butterfly valve mounted on the top of the valve chest. The 15in diameter flywheel was heavy enough for smooth running, the governed speed being usually 200 rpm. The remaining details should be clear from the drawing.

Sometimes a small horizontal was required for driving a side-show and that in Fig 345, all beautifully made and finished in brass on a wrought iron base, was used to drive a pump supplying water to a series of jets each supporting a small celluoid ball for a shooting booth. It has a cylinder 1¾in x 3½in and a flywheel 9in

Fig 345 Tidman horizontal engine in the author's possession.

(BY ROYAL   LETTERS PATENT.)

MEMORANDUM.

FROM

Robert * Tidman * and * Sons,

PATENTEES AND MANUFACTURERS   OF ALL KINDS OF

HAND AND STEAM POWER ROUNDABOUTS,

FITTED WITH OR WITHOUT OVERHEAD MOTION

For Galloping Horses and Suspended Platforms.

BISHOP BRIDGE IRON WORKS, NORWICH,

Mar. 6th   1890

Fig 346 Tidman letter heading and their nameplate.

diameter with a heavy rim. Drive to the pump was by a half-inch round leather belt, the pulley being outside the flywheel.

Inevitably, after a lapse of over forty years or more, records become scattered or lost and unfortunately none of Messrs. Tidman's order or despatch books have survived although a few drawings have been discovered which have proved most helpful in preparing these notes. I knew Robert Tidman, the grandson, very well, and many facts I have set down were gleaned from interesting conversations I enjoyed with him. All the family were skilled craftsmen and it was he who, when a young man, made the little engine in Fig 345. It is now a treasured possession in the author's collection. Robert Tidman reached an age in excess of eighty years and died during 1969 in Downham Market where in later years he resided with a married daughter. The firm never issued a catalogue as did their other competitors

and therefore I feel it appropriate to conclude with Fig 346 showing a reproduction of their letter heading together with their charming brass nameplate.

❧ XXXIX ❧

GEORGE WATERSON & CO., New Road Ironworks, NORTH WALSHAM.

A small concern flourishing in 1879 who advertised as makers of portable, vertical and horizontal engines and iron and brass founders.

No records seem to be available of their vertical and horizontal engines but an old illustration of the portable, not suitable for reproduction, shows it to have been of a design typical of this period with a single cylinder on the firebox, massive crankshaft bearing brackets, a large six-spoked flywheel and with a boiler feed pump fixed to the offside of the barrel and driven by an eccentric off the end of the crankshaft.

XL

JAMES WATTS,
Rose Lane Foundry, NORWICH.

James Watts, whom we have noticed in No XXXI, was one of the many country mechanics and ironfounders who displayed interest in steam on common roads and in early April 1832 he exhibited in Foundry Bridge Road, Norwich a small steam carriage of 2 nhp of his own design and construction. It was intended to use it between Norwich and Yarmouth and contemporary reports said that it did come up to the inventor's expectations. It is a pity no illustration has been discovered to show more details, and neither is it known what eventually happened to it.

Mr. Watts was certainly conversant with other steam carriages at this period such as those by Gurney, Hancock, Maceroni and Squire and others, for undoubtedly he embodied in his vehicle some proven details perfected by his contemporaries.

XLI

ARTHUR H. WEBBER & SONS LTD.,
Cobholm Engine Works, GREAT YARMOUTH.

A small firm established by Arthur Webber in 1889 who came from the famous firm of Whitmore & Binyon, steam engine builders of Wickham Market, Suffolk, to act as manager to Thomas Bradley (see No V) at the Bridge Foot Works, Southtown. In 1916 he acquired T. Lepard's premises (see No XXIV) in Cobholm where the firm continues in mechanical engineering.

Arthur Webber built a number of two-crank compound surface condensing engines in two sizes, the larger of which is depicted in Fig 347. These had cylinders 8in and 16in x 12in with web cranks and a multi-tubular surface condenser seen at the rear in the engraving. The smaller engines had cylinders 3½in and 7in x 6½in but with disc cranks.

The larger engines were installed in small cargo coasters and drifters and the latter size in smaller river boats. For example, the S.S. *Primrose* was fitted with Webber engines.

Fig 347 A. H. Webber's compact compound marine engine.

XLII

E. YOUNGS & CO. LTD.,
Waveney Ironworks & Swootman Foundry, Victoria Road, DISS.

First mention of Elijah Youngs is found in 1879 when he had a small works in Victoria Road known as the Waveney Ironworks. Later, he took into partnership the late George Unwin and the late W. Swootman, the latter having a small foundry known as the Swootman Foundry, also in Victoria Road, so that the address became as above. In 1924 the firm became a limited liability company and in May 1939 was acquired by Messrs. Sturgeon Brothers of Stanton, Suffolk. The final change took place in May 1947 when J. J. Wright & Son Ltd., the tractor repairers of East Dereham, obtained the business.

Elijah was another small maker of the homely portable and semi-portable, the total output being about a dozen engines. Fig 348 illustrates one of the first design. The boilers were of ample size for ready steaming. The jacketed single cylinder placed over the firebox had the valve chest on the left-hand side on which was placed the single Salter safety valve, the

spring rod of the scale being attached to an eye on the left-hand side of the outer crown plate. In some engines a round strut was fitted between the crankshaft bearing bracket and the cylinder on the left-hand side and a similar strut was used on the offside but was riveted to the firebox instead of being attached to the cylinder. The working pressure was 80 psi.

Later, an improved design was brought out and is depicted in Fig 349 and it will be seen that the pendulus governor has given place to a Hartnell Patent Shaft governor controlling the cut-offs of the slide valve. A continuous force pump with three valves is fixed immediately below the offside crankshaft bracket, combined with an exhaust feed water heater by means of which the boiler feed could be made almost boiling if required. All fireboxes were of best Lowmoor iron, the remainder of the boilers being of best quality steel plate and pressed to 100 psi.

Messrs. Youngs & Swootman declared that their

Fig 348 Elijah Young's first type of portable engine.

8 nhp engine would drive a 4ft 6in threshing and finishing machine with eight beaters and including elevator on about 5 hundredweights of good coals per day, executing a fair day's work. Another idea in the specification concerned the wheels and axles. The axles were turned and then case-hardened and with the wheel naves cast on a chill pin, provided with a screw cap to ensure oil-tightness and the exclusion of dirt. This later design was available in three sizes of 6, 8 and 10 nhp, the list prices just prior to World War 1 being £187, £217 and £250 respectively, the respective cylinders scaling 8in x 10in, 9in x 12in and 9½in x 12in. The last left the works in 1920.

A happy conclusion is afforded by the fact that the engine in Fig 349 is now preserved in working order in the Bloom Prytaneum of Mechanics at Bressingham.

Fig 349 Second design of portable made in Diss.

BIBLIOGRAPHY

Burrell Showman's Road Locomotives. Michael R. Lane.
Commercial Motor, The.
Chronicles of a Country Works. Ronald H. Clark.
Development of the English Traction Engine, The. Ronald H. Clark.
Development of the English Steam Wagon, The. Ronald H. Clark.
Eastern Daily Press.
Engineer, The.
Engineering.
Institution of Automobile Engineers. Proceedings.
Institution of Mechanical Engineers. Proceedings.
Locomotives of the Midland & Great Northern Joint Railway. Alan M. Wells.
Midland & Great Northern Joint Railway, A Short History of. Ronald H. Clark.
Midland & Great Northern Joint Railway Circle. Bulletins.
Motor Traction.
National Traction Engine Club. Journal (Steaming).
Newcomen Society, The. Transactions.
Norfolk Archaeology. Proceedings.
Norfolk Chronicle, The.
Road Locomotive Society. Journal.
Royal Agricultural Society. Transactions.
Savage, Frederick. David Braithwaite.
Savages Limited, 1850-1964. Ronald H. Clark.
Thetford Charities. George Bird Burrell.
Thetford & Watton Times.
World's Fair, The.
Together with many firm's Catalogues, Posters and Legal Documents, etc.

INDEX

References are to Figure Numbers

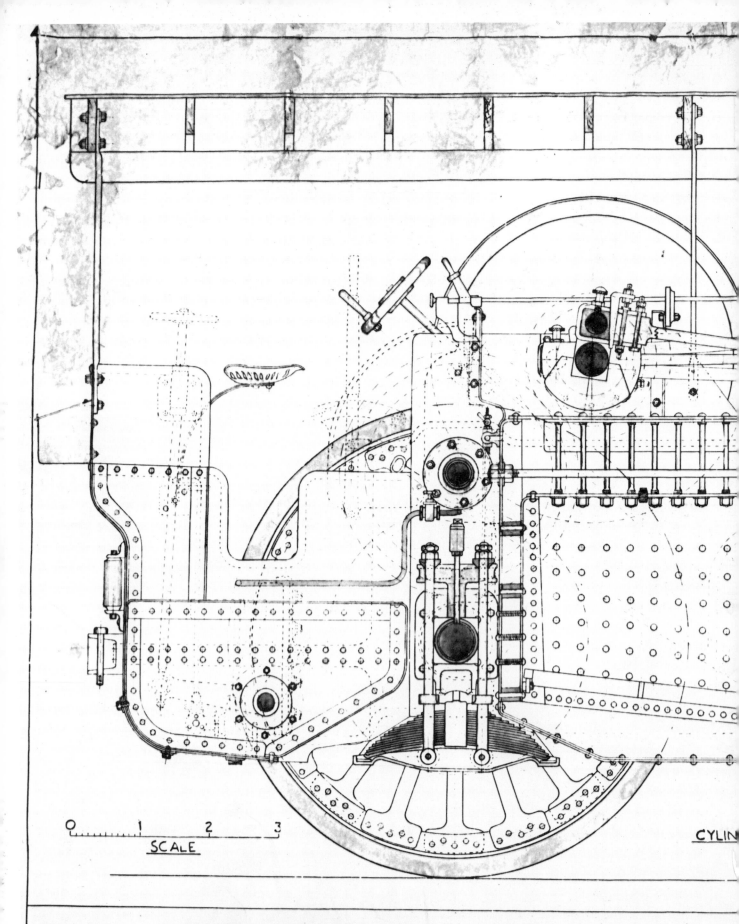

SCALE

0 1 2 3

CYLIN

BURRELL DOUBLE CRANK COMPOUND ROAD LOCOMOTIVE –